Developmental Brain Dysfunction

Published in collaboration with OASI Institute for Research on
Mental Retardation and Brain Aging, Troina (Italy)
Founded 1988 by E. Sega

KARGER

Developmental Brain Dysfunction
Printed in Italy by Litografia V.C.R. Srl

S. Karger AG,
Postfach, CH – 4009 Basel (Schweiz)

Appears bimonthly:
1 volume per year (6 issues)

Developmental Brain Dysfunction

Scope and Purposes: *Developmental Brain Dysfunction* is an international, multidisciplinary journal which rapidly publishes in English, original, high quality experimental and clinical research papers. The journal serves as a forum for scientific reports within the broad field of abnormal brain function particularly during development and aging (and including *normal* aging and development). Papers, either basic or clinical, on the genetic, anatomical, pathophysiological, biochemical or metabolic bases of impaired brain function as well as relating to responses of the nervous system to experimental interventions or pathologies and any attempts at experimentally modifying those responses are considered. Overriding criteria for acceptance of papers are sound scientific methodology, novelty, substantial experimental or clinical relevance, and interest to a multidisciplinary audience.

Types of Papers: The following types of papers, not previously published or being considered for publication elsewhere, will be considered.

Full-length papers reporting results of original research in areas within the scope and purpose of *Developmental Brain Dysfunction.* There is no page limit for these manuscripts but a maximum length of 15–20 printed pages is strongly encouraged.

Short communications including reports on research which has progressed to the stage when it is considered that the results should be made known rapidly to other workers in the field. The maximum length allowed is 2,000 words or equivalent space in tables and illustrations.

Review articles. These include review manuscripts and long research papers with extensive review components providing a comprehensive survey in a particular area within the scope of *Developmental Brain Dysfunction.* There is no length limitation for these reviews, but conciseness is strongly advised.

Submission: Manuscripts from Europe and Africa should be sent to:

Dr. R. Ferri
Developmental Brain Dysfunction
Oasi Institute for Research on
Mental Retardation and Brain Aging
Via Conte Ruggero, 73
I-94018 Troina (Italy)

Prof. A. Schinzel
Developmental Brain Dysfunction
Dept. of Medical Genetics
University of Zürich
Rämistrasse 74
CH-8001 Zürich (Switzerland)

From Asia and Oceania:
Prof. Y. Suzuki
Developmental Brain Dysfunction
The Tokyo Metropolitan Institute of
Medical Science
18–22, Honkomagome 3-chome
Bunkyo-ku, Tokyo 113 (Japan)

From the Americas:
Prof. J.R. Villablanca
Developmental Brain Dysfunction
Mental Retardation Research Center
Neuropsychiatric Institute
University of California, Los Angeles
Los Angeles, Ca 90024–1759 (USA)

Manuscripts should be submitted in quadruplicate (with four sets of illustrations of which two are originals), typewritten double-spaced on one side of the paper, with a wide margin.

Conditions: All manuscripts are subject to editorial review. Manuscripts are received with the explicit understanding that they are not under simultaneous consideration by any other publication. Submission of an article for publication implies the transfer of the copyright from the author to the publisher upon acceptance. Accepted papers become the permanent property of 'Developmental Brain Dysfunction' and may not be reproduced by any means, in whole or in part, without the written consent of the publisher and the Managing Editor. It is the author's responsibility to obtain permission to reproduce illustrations, tables, etc. from other publications.

Arrangement:

Title page: The first page of each paper should indicate the title (main title underlined), the authors' names, and the institute where the work was conducted. A short title for use as running head as well as the full address of the author to whom correspondence should be sent are also required.

Full address: The exact postal address complete with postal code must be given at the bottom of the title page. Please also supply phone and fax numbers.

Key words: For indexing purposes, a list of 3–10 key words in English is essential.

Abstract: Each paper needs an abstract of up to 10 lines.

Small type: Paragraphs which can or must be set in smaller type (case histories, test methods, etc.) should be indicated with a 'p' (petit) in the margin on the left-hand side.

Footnotes: Avoid footnotes. When essential, they are numbered consecutively and typed at the foot of the appropriate page.

Tables and illustrations: Tables and illustrations (both numbered in Arabic numerals) should be prepared on separate sheets. Tables require a heading and figures a legend, also prepared on a separate sheet. For the reproduction of illustrations, only good drawings and original photographs can be accepted; negatives or photocopies cannot be used. When possible, group several illustrations on one block for reproduction (max. size 140 × 188 mm) or provide crop marks. On the back of each illustration, indicate its number, the author's name, and 'top'. Color illustrations are reproduced at the author's expense.

References: In the text identify references by Arabic numerals [in square brackets]. Material submitted for publication but not yet accepted should be noted as 'unpublished data' and not be included in the reference list. The list of references should include only those publications which are cited in the text. Do not alphabetize; number references in the order in which they are first mentioned in the text. The surnames of the authors followed by initials should be given. There should be no punctuation other than a comma to separate the authors. Cite all authors, 'et al' is not sufficient. Abbreviate journal names according to the Index Medicus system. (Also see International Committee of Medical Journal Editors: Uniform requirements for manuscripts submitted to biomedical journals. Br Med J 1988;296:401–405.)

Examples

(a) Papers published in periodicals: Kauffman HF, van der Heide S, Beaumont F, Blok H, De Vries K: Class-specific antibody determination against *Aspergillus fumigatus* by means of the enzyme-linked immunosorbent assay. III. Comparative study: IgG, IgA, IgM ELISA titers, precipitating antibodies and IgE binding after fractionation of the antigen. Int Arch Allergy Appl Immunol 1986;80: 300–306.

(b) Monographs: Matthews DE, Farewell VT: Using and Understanding Medical Statistics. Basel, Karger, 1985.

(c) Edited books: Hardy WD Jr, Essex M: FeLV-induced feline acquired immune deficiency syndrome. A model for human AIDS; in Klein E (ed): Acquired Immunodeficiency Syndrome. Prog Allergy. Basel, Karger, 1986, vol 37, pp 353–376.

Further details: Authors may consult our leaflet 'Rules for the Preparation of Manuscripts', available on request from the Publisher, S. Karger AG, P.O. Box, CH-4009 Basel (Switzerland).

Galley proofs: Unless indicated otherwise, galley proofs are sent to the first-named author and should be returned with the least possible delay. Alterations made in galley proofs, other than the correction of printer's errors, are charged to the author. No page proofs are supplied.

Reprints: Order forms and a price list are sent with the galley proofs. Orders submitted after the issue is printed are subject to considerably higher prices. Allow five weeks from date of publication for delivery of reprints.

KARGER

General Information

Publication data: 'Developmental Brain Dysfunction' is published 6 times annually. Volume 6 with 6 issues appears in 1993.

Subscription rates: Subscriptions run for a full calendar year. Prices are given per volume.

Personal subscription:

Subscription	*+ postage and handling*
SFr. 261.10	+ SFr. 16.80 Europe
SFr. 261.10	+ SFr. 25.20 Overseas
US$ 174.30	+ US$ 16.80

(Must be in the name of, billed to, and paid by an individual. Order must be marked 'personal subscription').

Institutional subscription:

Subscription	*+ postage and handling*
SFr. 373.–	+ SFr. 24.– Europe
SFr. 373.–	+ SFr. 36.– Overseas
US$ 249.00	+ US$ 24.00

Airmail postage: SFr. 36.–, US$ 30.00. (Extra per volume.)

Microform edition: SFr. 186.50, US$ 124.50. (Available exclusively to subscribers of the paper edition.)

Subscription orders: Orders can be placed at agencies, bookstores, directly with the Publisher S. Karger AG, P.O. Box, CH-4009 Basel (Switzerland) or with any of the following distributors:

Deutschland: S. Karger GmbH
Lörracher Strasse 16A, Postfach
D-W-7800 Freiburg

France: Librairie Luginbühl
36, bd de Latour-Maubourg, F-75007 Paris

Great Britain, Ireland: S. Karger Publishers
11 Ravenscroft Road,
Beckenham, Kent BR3 4TP

USA: S. Karger Publishers, Inc.
26 West Avon Road, P.O. Box 529
Farmington, CT 06085

India, Bangladesh, Sri Lanka:
S. Karger India Subscription Agency
B-5/132 Safdarjung Enclave
New Delhi-110029

Japan: Katakura Libri, Inc.
36-9 Hongo 3-chome, Bunkyo-ku,
Tokyo 113

Change of address: Both old and new address should be sent to the subscription source.

Single issues: Information can be obtained through the Publisher.

Bibliographic indices: This journal is regularly listed in Reference Update and Excerpta Medica.

Advertising: Correspondence and rate requests should be addressed to the Publisher.

KARGER

Medicine and Sport Science (ISSN 0254–5020), **Vol. 36**
Series Editors: M. Hebbelinck, Brussels; R.J. Shephard, Toronto, Ont.

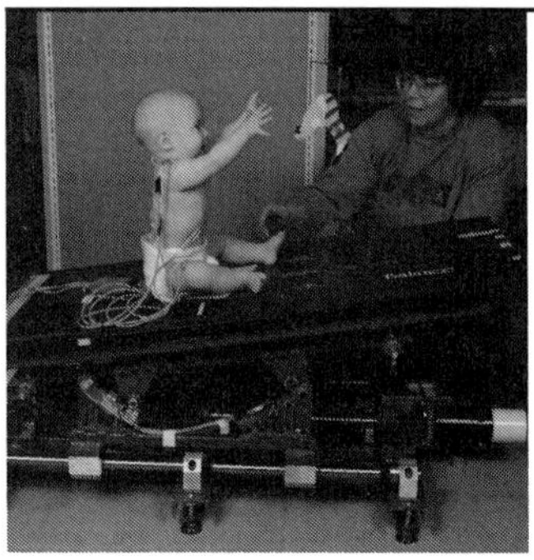

Editors: Hans Forssberg, Helga Hirschfeld

Movement Disorders in Children

This book is the first to transfer recently gained knowledge in neurobiology into new therapeutic concepts for improving motor control in children with movement disorders after early brain damage. The opening section covers therapeutic concepts both in traditional therapies and in newly developed motor control models. The following section deals with the effects of brain damage on the development of the central nervous system, especially in preterm babies, and considers the most appropriate type of treatment for infants. Further sections discuss motor mechanisms and perceptual processes in arm and hand movements as well as the implications for therapy of research in locomotion, spasticity and postural control. The final section considers the value and necessity of measurements, assessments and evaluations for occupational and physiotherapy diagnosis and intervention.
Stimulating and up-to-date, this multidisciplinary volume is an important source of knowledge for physiotherapists, occupational therapists and physicians in pediatric neurology and rehabilitation.

Contents

Fields of Interest
Sports Medicine; Pediatrics; Neurology; Logopedics, Medical Pedagogy, Neuropathology, Neurophysiology, Perinatal Medicine, Physiotherapy, Rehabilitation, Social and Preventive Medicine

Medicine and Sport Science, Vol. 36
Movement Disorders in Children
International Sven Jerring Symposium, Stockholm, August 1991
Editors: Forssberg, H.; Hirschfeld, H. (Stockholm)
VIII + 302 p., 53 fig., 11 tab., hard cover, 1992
SFr. 70.– / DM 84.– / US$ 56.00
Prices subject to change
DM price for FRG, US$ price for USA only
ISBN 3-8055-5556-3

KI 92575

KARGER

Impact of Prenatal Teratogenic Exposure on Phenotype and Brain Function

Editor:
Albert Schinzel, Zürich

Guest Reviewers:
L.A. Chasnoff, Chicago, IL
S. Clarren, Seattle, WA
M.J. Edwards, Sydney
B.J. Heckelöer, Hamburg
B. Hall, Lexington, KY
J. Hall, Vancouver
R. Huch, Zürich
S. Koch, Berlin
G. Koren, Toronto
F. Majewski, Düsseldorf
P. Meinecke, Hamburg
R. Michaelis, Tübingen
T.A. Slotkin, Durham, NC
W. Wertelecki, Mobile, AL
G. Wilson, Houston, TX

28 figures and 21 tables, 1993

KARGER

S. Karger · Medical and Scientific Publishers
Basel · Freiburg · Paris · London · New York · New Delhi · Bangkok · Singapore · Tokyo · Sydney

Drug Dosage

The authors and the publisher have exerted every effort to ensure that drug selection and dosage set forth in this text are in accord with current recommendations and practice at the time of publication. However, in view of ongoing research, changes in government regulations, and the constant flow of information relating to drug therapy and drug reactions, the reader is urged to check the package insert for each drug for any change in indications and dosage and for added warnings and precautions. This is particularly important when the recommended agent is a new and/or infrequently employed drug.

Printed in Italy on acid-free paper by
Litografia V.C.R. Srl
ISBN 3-8055-5791-4

Contents

Dev Brain Dysfunct 1993;6:197 – 198

Foreword

Teratogenic exposure is an increasingly recognized cause of congenital mental handicap. Unlike other forms of mental handicap, a great proportion of teratogenic damage is, at least theoretically, preventable. Thus, it is mandatory that physicians and patients at risk become aware of potential risk to which a fetus might be exposed. Information about such risks should, however, be given prior to conception thus allowing one to decide for or against a pregnancy and to provide the opportunity to get rid of the teratogenic agent prior to conception.

The present issue of *Developmental Brain Dysfunction* contains 7 articles, 6 of which deal with specific teratogens. Depending on the agent and the author, some of the articles are more clinically focused while others contain more data on experimental work. R.H. Finnell et al. (College Station, TX, USA) present an overview of the impact of maternal hyperthermia on fetal development in mouse and man. This issue was first raised by the unforgettable late David W. Smith some 15 years ago. Although the negative impact of hyperthermia on the developing fetus has long been known in mouse and other experimental animals, here was virtually no data available in man until Smith and subsequently others started to ask mothers of children with various sorts of congenital handicap specific questions on long-lasting fever, sauna bathing habits and long hot baths. The results, a positive correlation with the occurrence of neural tube defects and other brain defects, were first heavily criticized; the fact that sauna bathing could have an adverse effect irritated, among others, Finnish colleagues for whom the sauna is an institution of national pride. However, sauna habits in Finland are different from those in other parts of the world. Fortunately enough, Smith and others were not the men to be discouraged by such doubts. Thus, the investigations continued, and by now there is good evidence that early long-lasting hyperthermia might lead to congenital brain dysfunction, depending on factors such as duration, timing and temperature.

Since long maternal diabetes has been known to be a risk factor to the fetus, both for congenital defects and unspecific brain damage. The risk associated with duration of diabetes, renal and retinal involvement and other parameters is well known and has been the subject of other review papers before. E.J.H. Mulder (Utrecht, The Netherlands), in his paper in this issue, focuses on brain damage and its impact on fetal movements which could be a tool for prenatal ultrasonic investigations. Undoubtedly, as we know more about the normal fetal activity and its pathology, this approach could be applied not only to investigate fetuses of diabetic mothers, but, more importantly, those of alcohol-addicted mothers and of pregnancies at risk for fetal brain damage for which there is no other method of prenatal diagnosis.

R.M. Pauli and J.M. Haun (Madison, WI, USA), in the next paper, review the known facts concerning the impact of intrauterine exposure to coumarin derivatives. In Western countries, maintenance of oral anticoagulation into early pregnancy is probably the most frequent cause of induced abortion because of a high teratogenic risk to the fetus. The critical findings of coumarin-exposed newborns differ from those due to other exposures by its high specificity and the uniqueness of the clinical pattern. Pauli reviews the known facts about possible mechanisms of coumarin damage to the fetal tissues and the implication of this to risk estimation with respect to the period of exposure.

The next paper, by F. Majewski (Düsseldorf, Germany), reviews the sequelae to the fetus of chronic alcohol abuse during pregnancy and adds new data from an expanded clinical review. The author runs one of the largest, if not the largest, clinics with patients with this condition in the world. For Majewski, only fetuses of mothers who are both physically and mentally addicted to alcohol for a long period are at risk for alcohol damage. The risk also depends on, and damage correlates with, duration of alcohol addiction, amount of alcohol ingested, and other confounding factors. However, for Majewski, the stage of alcoholism in the mother is the most important factor. This opinion is based on personal experience not only with families with probands with the fetal alcohol syndrome and fetal alcohol effects, but, of course, also from observations of heavy alcohol consumption, either as binge drinking or as consumpion throughout a long period of the pregnancy without any fetal damage. It disagrees, however, with observations of other, mostly American, observers.

The teratogenic sequelae of intrauterine exposure to diphenylhydantoin derivatives has repeatedly been reviewed, and a mouse model has been established. Many other antiepileptic drugs have similar metabolic pathways, and thus their teratogenic effects might be similar or even identical as proposed by several authors. Carbamazepine is one of the few compounds used in antiepileptic treatment, which is totally different from the former, and it was long considered as the safest antiepileptic for the fetus. V. Vestermark (Copenhagen, Denmark), reviewing newer literature and her own observation to this point, arrives at the conclusion that, in principle, this still holds true. However, carbamazepine might induce minor anomalies in the fetus and increase the risk for spina bifida, especially if the compound is given in combination with one or more other antiepileptics.

The sixth paper, by W. Lichtensteiger and M. Schlumpf (Zürich, Switzerland), focuses on observed differences in behavior between children prenatally exposed to the products ingested during cigarette smoking and controls. Among those, nicotine presumably plays a major role, and the pharmacological and biochemical developmental pathways after nicotine exposure to the developing brain are reviewed by the authors. Of course, other effects of cigarette exposure, notably decreased birthweight and a tendency to prematurity and adaptation difficulties at birth, are probably not explained solely by nicotine alone, and especially oxygen depletion will play a major role for their occurrence.

The last paper is the most practical one and is not confined to one teratogenic agent. G. Koren and I. Nulman (Toronto, Canada) present an overview over published reports on potential developmental defects in fetuses exposed to potential teratogens which could be visualized by prenatal ultrasonography. Only few teratogenics are proven to increase the incidence of major malformations of certain organs or organ systems; however, as such an increase can hardly be excluded for many potential teratogens, it is necessary for the obstetricians controlling the pregnancy of a teratogen-exposed pregnant woman to know of which potential malformations he has to be aware. Although it could be argued that a thorough ultrasound is indicated in any pregnancy, and especially in a pregnancy with a potentially increased risk for congenital fetal malformations, it is obviously of practical use to have some hints as to which fetal structures have to be especially controlled and for what type of anomalies.

A paper dealing with the teratogenic effects of methadone exposure, which originally was planned for this special issue will appear in one of the next issues of *Developmental Brain Dysfunction*.

Albert Schinzel, Zürich

Dev Brain Dysfunct 1993;6:199–209

The Impact of Maternal Hyperthermia on Morphogenesis: Clinical and Experimental Evidence for a Fetal Hyperthermia Phenotype

Richard H. Finnell, Laura E. Taylor, Gregory D. Bennett

Department of Veterinary Anatomy and Public Health, College of Veterinary Medicine, Texas A & M University, College Station, TX, USA

Key Words. Hyperthermia · Congenital malformations · Neural tube defects · Epidemiology · Teratogenicity

Abstract. The adverse reproductive consequences of in utero exposure to elevated temperature were documented in experimental animal species over 30 years ago. More recently, the possibility that maternal hyperthermia, either secondary to a febrile episode or due to prolonged exposure in a hot tub or sauna bath, may be teratogenic in humans has been the subject of intense investigation. Reviewing the human clinical and epidemiologic literature, the data suggests that maternal hyperthermia during early organogenesis can result in an increased risk for certain congenital malformations. The type and frequency of these defects vary with the timing and duration of the exposure period, data that are confirmed in the experimental animal literature.

Introduction

The adverse effects of maternal hyperthermia on embryonic development have been widely appreciated for almost 30 years now, based on the seminal work of Edwards [1]. However, only since the late 1970's has the medical community come to recognize in utero hyperthermic exposure to be a potential human teratogen. This recognition was largely the result of a number of anecdotal clinical reports published by the late Professor Smith et al. [2] at the University of Washington, as well as selected retrospective epidemiologic studies. Although it has been argued that humans are homeothermic, and are therefore able to withstand wide fluctuations in temperature, the literature suggests that as small an elevation as 1.5–2.5 °C in the maternal core temperature is sufficient to disrupt normal morphogenesis [1, 5]. Such temperaure elevations in humans are not uncommon events, resulting either from a pathogenic agent inducing a febrile episode, or an environmental exposure to high exogenous temperatures, such as those associated with

Table 1. Congenital malformations in offspring exposed in utero to excessive maternal hyperthermia

Abnormality	Study format						
	retrospective		clinical				prospective
	Fraser and Skelton [9]	Shiota [13]	Smith et al. [3]	Pleet et al. [5]	Fisher and Smith [4]	Superneau and Wertelecki [6]	Little et al. [15]
CNS: structural							
neuronal heterotopias	–	–	–	+	–	–	–
microphthalmia	+	–	+	+	+	–	–
microcephaly	+	–	+	+	–	–	–
anencephaly	+	+	+	–	+	–	–
myeloschisis/encephalocele	–	+	–	–	+	–	–
holoprosencephaly	–	+	–	–	–	–	–
CNS: functional							
mental deficiency	+	–	–	+	+	–	–
hypotonicity	+	–	+	+	+	–	–
hypertonicity	–	–	–	+	+	–	–
seizures	+	–	+	–	+	–	–
Facial							
micrognathia	+	–	–	+	–	+	–
midfacial hypoplasia	–	–	+	+	+	–	–
external ear anomalies	–	–	+	+	–	–	–
cleft lip +/– palate	–	–	+	+	–	–	–
Other							
genital	+	–	–	+	–	–	–
gastro/abdominal body wall	–	+	–	–	–	–	+
limb/digital defects	+	+	+	+	–	+	–

certain occupation environments or exposures of a recreational (sauna or hot tub) variety. Given that developmental defects were observed in all animal species (guinea pigs, mice, rats, chicks, and monkeys) examined to date when core or incubation temperature elevations were 2 °C or more above normal levels, there was no reason to suspect that human embryos were significantly more heat resistant [1]. In this article, we intend to review the fundamental experimental and clinical literature in order to provide an overview of the teratogenic effects of elevated temperature on the phenotype of the developing conceptus.

Clinical Studies

As is often the case with the recognition of potential human teratogens, astute clinical observations published as case reports provide the first suggestion of a possible association between in utero exposure to elevated temperatures and an increased risk for congenital defects. One of these early studies described a small series of patients that had been exposed to maternal hyperthermia during gestational weeks 4 – 6. The patients presented with a series of congenital defects, including distal limb anomalies, facial dysmorphia, hypotonia and were severely mentally retarded [2]. In a follow-up clinical series in which exposure to a hyperthermic insult occurred during weeks 4 – 8 after conception, Fisher and Smith [43] described infants with occipital encephaloceles, mental deficiency, distal limb defects, and a pattern of facial dysmorphogenesis which included: microphthalmia, midfacial hypoplasia, micrognathia and external ear anomalies (table 1). Similarly, Pleet et al. [5] documented a very high incidence of mental retardation and microphthalmia secondary to a hyperthermic exposure during weeks 4 – 7 of gestation (table 1). This study failed to observe any adverse effects of hyperthermia when the exposure period occurred in the latter half of gestation [5]. More recently, Superneau and Wertelecki [6] described 2 children in which the mother experienced a febrile illness during the 10th week of gestation (table 1). Both children had oromandibular and limb abnormalities which were likened to those produced experimentally in the hyperthermic guinea pig models [7, 8]. The clinical studies provide the best evidence for the extent of the phenotypical alterations that may, in fact, be the result of teratogenic hyperthermic insult during critical periods of development.

Retrospective Studies

In one of the earliest of the retrospective analyses of congenital malformations secondary to maternal hyperthermia exposure, Fraser and Skelton [9] reviewed the hospital records of every fifth child born with a congenital defect, cerebral palsy, or mental retardation at the Montreal Children's Hospital. In the 479 study subjects that had records documenting maternal fever status throughout gestation (either positive or negative), these investigators found a highly significant increase in microphthalmia amongst the 55 infants who were exposed to a hyperthermic episode during the first 5 months of pregnancy. Of the 5 cases with microphthalmia, 3 infants were also profoundly mentally retarded. In a follow-up study, the records of 1,688 infants with congenital defects were obtained from the same hospital. As seen in table 1, in addition to mental deficiency, those malformations observed with the highest frequency that were associated with a recorded febrile event in the first 5 months of pregnancy were hypospadias, microphthalmia, and cardiac defects [10]. In a retrospective study of infants born with anencephaly, Miller et al. [11] noted that 7 out of 63 anencephalic pregnancies had a positive history for maternal hyperthermia in excess of 38.9 °C. Of these 7 cases, a febrile illness was determined as the cause of the hyperthermia in 5 of the mothers, while recreational sauna use was reported in the other 2 cases. The highly significant incidence of hyperthermic exposure observed in the mothers of anencephalic infants represented in excess of a 100-fold increase over that reported in control populations.

Two other noteworthy retrospective studies were published in the early 1980's by Layde et al. [12] and Shiota [13]. In a Center for Disease Control study, the investigators interviewed mothers with selected congenital defects within 6 months of the child's birth in order to minimize the deleterious effects of recall biases and maximize the quality of the exposure information obtained. They observed a highly significant association between spina bifida and maternal fever, defined as either a recorded febrile illness or an explicity mentioned febrile episode in the first trimester [12]. However, there was no significant association between maternal hyperthermia and anterior neural tube defects (NTDs) in this epidemiologic study. The work by Shiota [13] utilized autopsy information from a human embryo collection that was supplemented by a maternal obstetrical history which was obtained either immediately before or directly after the termination procedure in order to minimize potential maternal memory bias. The results obtained in this study supported the hypothesis that maternal hyperthermia could induce anterior neural tube defects in developing fetuses, yet lacked any positive association between maternal febrile illness and spina bifida (table 1).

Most recently, Erickson [14] interviewed parents of 4,900 infants with major congenital malformations as well as the parents from 300 nonaffected neonates and observed 50 highly significant associations between maternal exposure and specific malformations. Of these, 27 significant associations were made between a maternal febrile illness and congenital malformations of the CNS, including both anterior and posterior NTDs [14].

Prospective Studies

Prospective data is much more limited than either the clinical or retrospective data with regards to the developmental consequences of in utero exposure to elevated temperatures during gestation. The most recent of these studies involved 54 women who reported having experienced a fever in excess of 38.9 °C for at least 24 h during the first trimester of pregnancy [15]. Control women were matched at the same hospital by the time of the pregnancy, parity and maternal age. In this study, the overall malformation rates did not differ between the study and the control groups; however, the frequency of abdominal wall defects including diastasis rectus and herniated umbilicus were significantly higher in the hyperthermia exposure group [15]. While this study did not find the previously reported association between first-trimester hyperthermic insult and an increased incidence of NTDs, the authors did conclude that there is a significant risk for congenital malformations in the exposed offspring.

Summary of Human Studies

Not all of the retrospective and prospective epidemiologic studies conducted to date support the hypothesis that in utero exposure to maternal hyperthermia is teratogenic and therefore processes a significant reproductive risk to the CNS of exposed fetuses. Editorials in such prestigious medical journals as *Lancet* and the *British Medical Journal* argued against the existence of convincing evidence that maternal hyperthermia causes developmental defects in humans [16, 17]. These editorials maintain that only a very small percentage of infants with NTDs had a hyperthermic exposure in the first trimester. Furthermore, the exceedingly low rate of NTDs in Finland, where women routinely take saunas even while pregnant, argues against any causal relationship between hyperthermia and congenital malformations. It bears mentioning that Finnish women routinely limit the duration of their saunas, and most likely never elevate their core temperature to a sufficient degree to induce congenital defects [18]. Although the critical temperature for the induction of a congenital malformation may vary amongst individuals, in a study to determine the effects of sauna on core temperature in nonpregnant women, not 1 of the test subjects could tolerate the heat exposure long enough to raise their core temperature to 38.9 °C [19]. In this same study, it was observed that the women could sustain exposure to a 39 °C hot tub exposure for at least 15 min, or a 41 °C hot tub for 10 min, without raising their core temperature to a teratogenic level [19]. On the other hand, a study by Sohar et al. [20] demonstrated that exposure to a sauna whose temperature was between 80 and 90 °C produced core temperature elevations exceeding 39 °C in 22% of the test subjects, and that this elevated body temperature persisted beyond 20 min in 16% of the study participants. It may well be that recreational sauna and hot tub use during pregnancy do not substantially increase the risk for producing an infant with a congenital defect, yet one cannot rule out the possibility that sauna or hot tub use during critical periods of development can induce maternal hyperthermia that directly leads to the production of congenital abnormalities.

The negative data are not limited to studies where the hyperthermia was linked to exogenous environmental effects. Kleinbrecht et al. [21] did not observe any significant correlation between congenital malformations and maternal febrile illness during pregnancy in their retrospective case control study. They examined over 2,300 infants with NTDs and found but 17 who had a positive history of maternal hyperthermia during the critical period of gestation. This was not significantly different from the rate of hyperthermia exposure in the control group of nonaffected infants [21]. Similarly, Clarren et al. [22] examined Collaborative Perinatal Project data in which 165 women had reported a febrile episode that was documented to exceed the 38.9 °C threshold during the first trimester. The offspring of these women did not differ from control infants with respect to stillbirths, prematurity, growth patterns, neurological deformities and intelligence [22]. However, using essentially the same Collaborative Perinatal Project data base, Sever [23] found that 5.2% of the study women had viral infections during pregnancy, while 1.5% had urinary tract infections which likely produced a febrile episode. The children of these pregnancies were found to be twice as likely to have neurological problems as did the children of control mothers. Thus, while regrettably incomplete, we believe that the evidence strongly suggests that maternal hyperthermia is a human teratogen whose primary target is the developing nervous system. This conclusion is based directly upon the existing clinical data taken in light of the strong body of experimental animal literature (see below), although dissenting opinions, such as those of Warkany [24] who reviewed the hyperthermia literature and concluded that no causal connection could be made between in utero hyperthermia exposure and congenital malformations, will always continue to persist. Nevertheless, many investigators strongly believe that there exists sufficient evidence for the inclusion of several characteristic features to form the basis of a hyperthermic syndrome, including mental retardation, microcephaly, facial dysmorphism, club foot and arthrogryposis [3, 25] (table 1). In light of the existing controversy, it is imperative to draw upon the experimental evidence when attempting to make reasoned judgements concerning the teratogenicity of hyperthermia.

Experimental Animal Studies

Hyperthermia has been shown experimentally to be detrimental to developing organisms, since Goldschmidt [26] demonstrated that exposing *Drosophila* larvae to elevated temperatures resulted in the production of phenocopies. Early studies by Hsu [27], Kreshover and Clough [28] and MacFarlane et al. [29] in rats demonstrated the adverse impact of early embryonic exposure to elevated temperatures on the development of ocular and dental structures. Since this time, hyperthermia has proven to be teratogenic in species as diverse as birds, rodents, and nonhuman primates. What is abundantly clear from these studies is that the same pattern of malformations is observed depending upon the timing and intensity of the hyperthermic treatment.

Although most of the experimental studies have been performed on one of the rodent species, a few investigations have made excellent use of other domestic species. An example of one such study involved incubating chicken eggs at 39.4 °C, which is 2.4 °C above the normal incubation temperature. This treatment resulted in an elevated incidence of embryolethality and nervous system defects when compared to eggs incubated at control temperatures [30]. The type of nervous system defects observed were similar to defects induced by viral infections, leading the authors to speculate that in cases where a viral infection was suspected as contributing to a teratogenic outcome, it may be the elevation in temperature and not the virus that was primarily responsible for the observed developmental defect [30].

The guinea pig was the original species used to investigate the teratogenic potential of hyperthermia in mammals. Heating pregnant guinea pig dams for 1 h at 43.3 °C on gestational days 18 – 26 caused both structural as well as behavioral abnormalities [7]. This treatment caused the maternal core temperature to increase by 3.9 °C and induced an array of defects which included: microcephaly, hydranencephaly, defects of the abdominal wall, amyoplasia and hypoplasia of the lateral digits [7]. Malformations of the brain and skeletal system were the most commonly observed defects. It was noted that a higher incidence of malformations was induced if the treatment was administered during the early stages of gestation. Furthermore, if hyperthermia-treated dams were allowed to deliver their pups, behavioral deficits were observed in the offspring [7]. These neonatal guinea pigs were slow in movement, unable to stand, uncoordinated, slow to suckle, and died neonatally due to starvation. This behavioral defect may actually be secondary to an underlying morphological defect, in that it appears that hyperthermia has a propensity to cause nervous system abnormalities.

Hamster embryos manifest the same response to a prenatal hyperthermic exposure as was observed in the guinea pig, with NTDs being the most commonly observed defects. If the pregnant dam was exposed to a 40 – 41 °C environment for 1 – 1.25 h on gestational day 8 of development, the progeny have an elevated incidence of exencephaly and encephaloceles [31]. This treatment also resulted in a high percentage of embryo lethality (8 – 82%) which was duration and temperature dependent. This was also true of the malformation rate; as the temperature and/or the duration of exposure were increased, so were the malformations [31]. If the treatment protocol was altered to include two 20-min treatments at 40 °C that were 6 h apart on the same day, then the peak period for the induction of cranial malformations was observed to occur on gestational day 9 [32]. Exencephaly was observed following treatments early in gestation, days 6 – 10, while cleft lip and palate appeared if the pregnant dam was treated on gestational days 9 or 10. Limb malformations were induced following exposure on gestational days 9 – 11. The peak period of sensitivity, for these limb defects, proved to be day 11. The number of affected offspring with limb malformations increased from gestational day 9 – 11; however, if the dam was treated on day 10, the hindlimb was affected more often than the forelimb. As seen with the single treatment group in the Kilham and Ferm [31] study, resorption rates varied with this multiple treatment protocol. Not surprisingly, day 7 of gestation was shown to be the most sensitive period with 52.6% of the litters being resorbed [32].

As most of the in vivo hyperthermia studies have been performed by exposing the pregnant dam to elevated temperatures, this protocol raises some questions as to whether maternal toxicity plays an important role in the etiology of the observed defects. A further concern was whether or not recording maternal core temperatures was an accurate account of the actual embryonic hyperthermic exposure or stress. To address these questions, Skreb and Frank [33] directly exposed rat embryos to elevated temperatures in utero. Under anesthesia, the abdominal wall was opened and one horn of the uterus was placed in a warm saline bath set at 40 – 41 °C for 40, 60, or 90 min. The other uterine horn remained in the dam and served as a control for these experiments. They observed a peak period of sensitivity to the induction of NTDs and embryolethality. When the treatment was administered on gestational day 7.5, no malformations were observed; however, the resorption rate increased as the treatment duration increased from 40 to 90 min. Treatment on day 8.5 of gestation caused approximately 5.5% of the offspring to be malformed when they were heated for either 40 or 60 min. In contrast, the resorption rate was 21.8% with a treatment of 40 min but increased to 70.6% with a 60-min treatment. If the pregnant dam was treated a day later, day 9.5, this treatment induced 12.2 and 9.2 malformations and 27 and 64% resorptions at 40 and 60 min, respectively. In this study, treatments after 9.5 days of gestation were no longer significantly teratogenic. The structural malformations observed in this study were of the nervous system and facial structures, including anophthalmia, microphthalmia, and anencephaly [33]. Although the response frequencies of the observed malformations in this study were less than in studies where the pregnant dam was directly treated, the treatment temperatures used in this study (40 – 41 °C) were lower than in studies where the dam was heated (43 °C). Still, this study serves to validate the other studies where the pregnant dam was directly heated, for the malformations observed were similar irrespective of the treatment protocol.

Another approach that was applied to determine whether or not maternal toxicity plays a role in the observed hyperthermia-induced malformations was to expose embryos to a hyperthermic insult in vitro. Using explanted gestational-day-10 embryos and culturing them for 46 – 48 h, including a mild hyperthermia (40 or 41 °C) treatment of various durations, Cockroft and New [34] observed severe developmental abnormalities. Although over half of the embryos cultured at 41 °C were microcephalic and somite formation was so poor that somite counts could not be made, there was also a definite teratogenic effect at the lower temperature. If cultured embryos were exposed to 41 °C only during the initial stages (the first 12 – 24 h of the culture period, the embryos appeared to be exceptionally sensitive, manifesting microcephaly, pericardial edema as well as effects of the blood circulation, rotation of the embryo and fusion of the allantois and chorion [34]. This study demonstrates that even a relatively mild increase in temperature (2 – 3 °C) can cause significant deleterious effects in the developing embryo, as well as illustrating that maternal toxicity may play only a minor role in the malformations observed following a prenatal hyperthermic exposure.

A dose response to maternal hyperthermia was examined in detail by treating pregnant dams on gestational day 9.5 at several temperatures and for different durations [35]. If the core temperature of the dam was elevated to 43.5 °C and then brought back to 37 °C, a spike-hyperthermic exposure, all the surviving fetuses had microphthalmia, and 45% had encephaloceles. However, a spike treatment that resulted in a core temperature of 43 °C induced only 7% microphthalmia. If the dam was maintained at 43 °C for 2 min, the frequency of microphthalmia increased to 42%, while 14% of the fetuses had large encephaloceles. A 5-min exposure was embryolethal to the majority of the fetuses (66%) and 97% of those that did survive had encephaloceles and cleft faces. Decreasing the exposure temperature to 42.5 °C proved to be teratogenic only if the dam was heated for longer than 5 min. A 10- to 20-minute exposure produced encephaloceles, microphthalmia, and cleft face in most of the fetuses. Temperatures below 42 °C were rarely teratogenic, unless the exposure time was dramatically increased. The malformations observed at these lower temperatures were the same as those seen at higher temperatures, only now they appeared at significantly lower response frequencies. This study clearly illustrates that there was a dose response not only to the treatment temperature, but also to the duration of the treatment [35].

The correlation between a rise of 35 °C in maternal core temperature and fetal nervous system defects has also been shown to occur even by indirect heating of the pregnant dam. In an effort to determine the effects of radiofrequency radiation (microwave) on development, pregnant rats were subjected to 27.12 MHz of radiation until the maternal core temperature reached 43 °C [36]. This temperature elevation required an exposure period of 20 – 40 min. Again, as shown in other studies, treatments on or about day 9 of gestation induced the greatest frequency of congenital defects which were primarily restricted to the anterior region of the developing organism. Thus, irrespective of the mechanism involved, directly or indirectly elevating the core body temperature of the pregnant dam by 3 – 5 °C induces NTDs in the exposed offspring.

The genetic basis of susceptibility to hyperthermia-induced NTDs was examined in a mouse model in which the animals were partially submerged in a 43 °C waterbath. Using dams from several different inbred strains during the period of neural tube closure in the mouse, Finnell et al. [37] reproducibly induced varying degrees of exencephaly, depending upon the strain of the mouse and the gestational timing of the treatment. On gestational day 8.5, the period of peak sensitivity, there was a hierarchy of susceptibility with response frequencies ranging from the completely resistant DBA/2J strain (0%) to the highly sensitive SWV/Fnn strain, in which 44.3% of the fetuses had NTDs [37]. This variation in the response frequencies suggests that there is a strong genetic component in determining susceptibility to heat-induced exencephaly. This was further determined in reciprocal cross studies between strains of high (SWV), moderate (LM/Bc) and low (C57BL/6J) sensitivity. The results of these breeding studies demonstrate that the high response rate of the SWV/Fnn strain is rapidly lost in the F_1 hybrids outcrosses to either of the test strains. The fact that the F_1 fetuses had response frequencies similar to the low-sensitivity parental strains suggests that the genetic basis for high sensitivity to hyperthermia-induced NTDs involves only a few genes that are unique to the SWV/Fnn strain [37]. Equally important was the finding that it was the embryo's genotype, and not that of the mother, that was the critical factor in determining susceptibility to heat-induced NTDs.

Experimental studies on the adverse effects of maternal hyperthermia on embryonic development were not limited to rodents or chickens. Studies of hyperthermia and NTDs have also been conducted in nonhuman primates. Bonnet monkeys which were exposed to a hyperthermic treatment on gestational days 24–27 that elevated the maternal core temperature by 3.9 °C resulted in fetuses with midfacial hypoplasia and severe growth retardation [38]. A single treatment on day 26 produced major malformations of the skeleton, heart, and brain. Specifically, the brain possessed only rudimentary (meroanencephaly) structures. The sensitive period was shown to be between day 23 and 29 of gestation, for there were normal births following heat treatments before and after this time [38]. This study also suggested that vascular disruptions might play a role in the heat-induced NTDs for it was noted that the placentas from the heat-treated dams had a high incidence of surface infarction and intervillous thrombi [38]. Although vascular disruption is one widely accepted mechanism for a variety of congenital abnormalities [39, 40], to what extent this is of importance in the observed malformations remains unknown.

The evidence from the existing experimental animal literature suggests that all animal species including birds, laboratory animal, and nonhuman primates exposed to experimentally induced hyperthermic insult during critical periods of morphogenesis produces a comparable pattern of malformations that is dose and timing related. This serves to further support the clinical observations that maternal hyperthermia is a potent teratogenic agent. Although the ultimate proof that an agent is a human teratogen must be sought in human studies [41], given the experimental animal evidence, it would be difficult to imagine that human embryos were not subject to similar adverse developmental consequences.

Summary and Conclusion

While lacking complete unanimity in terms of the acceptance of maternal hyperthermia as a significant human teratogen, the overwhelming evidence supports the hypothesis that an elevation of the maternal core temperature by as little as 1.5–2.5 °C during critical periods of neurulation and early organogenesis can alter normal morphogenetic pathways and result in the production of offspring with serious congenital malformations. The phenotype of the affected infant is variable, but the nervous system appears to be the primary target, with mental retardation, microcephaly, microphthalmia, facial dysmorphia and neurogenic arthrogryposis being the most consistently observed abnormalities in the constellation of hyperthermia-induced defects (table 1). It has also been suggested that hyperthermic exposure could produce a phenocopy of the Moebius syndrome by a vascular compromise of the uterine circulation [42]. Although theoretically plausible, based upon the experimental animal literature, the 3 cases presented by Lipson et al. [42] are sufficient evidence to satisfactorily conclude that maternal hyperthermia may be responsible for specific, 'localizing' effects in the developing fetus. The maternal hyperthermia could be secondary to a febrile episode of various pathogenetic etiologies, or due to an exogenous elevation in the ambient temperature surrounding the mother. However, given the evidence on thermoregulation in exercise and in occupational studies, it is highly unlikely that serious strenuous training or recreational use of hot tubs and saunas would be of sufficient intensity and/or duration to increase the maternal core temperature to the point at which the embryo's developmental sequence is at risk [43, 44]. Nonetheless, a certain degree of prudence is advised for the pregnant patient concerning these endeavors during the period of CNS formation.

Acknowledgements

This project was supported in part by NIH grant ES04326 and a Biomedical Research Support Grant.

References

1 Edwards MJ, Wanner RA: Extremes of temperature; in Wilson JG, Fraser FC (eds): Handbook of Teratology. Plenum Press, New York, 1977, vol 1, pp 421–444.
2 Edwards MJ: Hyperthermia as a teratogen: A review of experimental studies and their clinical significance. Teratog Carcinog Mutag 1986;6: 563–582.
3 Smith DW, Clarren SK, Harvey MAS: Hyperthermia as a possible teratogenic agent. J Pediatr 1978;92:878–883.
4 Fisher NL, Smith DW: Occipital encephalocele and early gestational hyperthermia. Pediatrics 1981;68: 480–483.
5 Pleet H, Graham JM Jr, Smith DW: Central nervous system and facial defects associated with maternal hyperthermia at four to 14 weeks' gestation. Pediatrics 1981;67:785–789.
6 Superneau DW, Wertelecki W: Similarity of effects – Experimental hyperthermia as a teratogen and maternal febrile illness associated with oromandibular and limb defects. Am J Med Genet 1985;21:575–580.
7 Edwards MJ: Congenital defects in guinea pigs. Arch Pathol 1967;84:42–48.
8 Edwards MJ: Congenital malformations in the rat following induced hyperthermia during gestation. Teratology 1968;1:173–178.
9 Fraser FC, Skelton J: Possible teratogenicity of maternal fever. Lancet 1978;ii:634.
10 Spragget K, Fraser FC: Teratogenicity of maternal fever in women – A retrospective study. Teratology 1982;25:78A.
11 Miller P, Smith DW, Shepard TH: Maternal hyperthermia as a possible cause of anencephaly. Lancet 1978:i:519–520.
12 Layde PM, Edmonds LD, Erickson JD: Maternal fever and neural tube defects. Teratology 1980;21:105–108.
13 Shiota K: Neural tube defects and maternal hyperthermia in early pregnancy: Epidemiology in a human embryonic population. Am J Med Genet 1982;12:281–288.
14 Erickson JD: Risk factors for birth defects: Data from the Atlanta birth defects case-control study. Teratology 1991;43:41–51.
15 Little BB, Ghali FE, Snell LM, Knoll KA, Johnston W, Gilstrapp LC III: Is hyperthermia teratogenic in the human? Am J Perinatol 1991; 8:185–189.
16 Anonymous Editorial: Hyperthermia and neural tube defects. Lancet 1978;ii:560–561.

17 Anonymous Editorial: Is hyperthermia a teratogen? Br Med J 1978;256:1586–1587.
18 Saxen L, Holmberg PC, Nurminen M, Kuosma E: Sauna and congenital defects. Teratology 1982;25:309–313.
19 Harvey MAS, McRorie M, Smith DW: Suggested limits to the use of hot tubs and sauna by pregnant women. Can Med Assoc J 1981;125:50–54.
20 Sohar E, Shoenfeld Y, Shapiro Y, Ohry A, Cabili S: Effects of exposure to Finnish sauna. Isr J Med Sci 1976;12:1275–1282.
21 Kleinbrecht J, Michaelius H, Michaelis J, Koller S: Fever in pregnancy and congenital defects. Lancet 1979;i:1403.
22 Clarren SK, Smith DW, Harvey MAS, Ward RH, Myrianthopoulos NC: Hyperthermia – A prospective evaluation of a possible teratogenic agent in man. J Pediatr 1979;95:81–83.
23 Sever JL: Infection in pregnancy. Teratology 1982; 25:227–237.
24 Warkany J: Teratogen update: Hyperthermia. Teratology 1986;33:365–371.
25 Ivarsson SA, Henricksson P: Septic shock and hyperthermia as possible teratogenic factors. Acta Paediatr Scand 1984;73:875–879.
26 Goldschmidt R: Gen und Ausseneigenschaft (Untersuchungen an Drosophila) I und II. Z Indukt Abstammungs-Vererbungsl 1935;69:38–131.
27 Hsu CY: Influence of temperature on development of rat embryos. Anat Rec 1948;100:79–87.
28 Kreshover SJ, Clough OW: Prenatal influences on tooth development. 11. Artificially induced fever in rats. J Dent Res 1953;32:565–570.
29 MacFarlane WV, Pennycuik PR, Thrift E: Resorption, and loss of fetuses in rats living at 35 °C. J Physiol 1957;135:451–460.
30 De La Cruz MV, Campillo-Sainz C, Munoz-Armas S: Congenital heart defects in chick embryos subjected to temperature variations. Çirc Res 1966; 18:257–262.
31 Kilham L, Ferm VH: Exencephaly in fetal hamsters following exposure to hyperthermia. Teratology 1976:14:323–326.
32 Umpierre CC, Dukelow WR: Environmental heat stress in the hamster. Teratology 1978;16:155–158.
33 Skreb N, Frank Z: Developmental abnormalities in the rat induced by heatshock. J Embryol Exp Morphol 1963;11:445–457.
34 Cockcroft DL, New DAT: Effect of hyperthermia on rat embryos in culture. Nature 1975;258:604–606.
35 Germain MA, Webster WS, Edwards MJ: Hyperthermia as a teratogen: Parameters determining hyperthermia-induced head defects in the rat. Teratology 1985;31:265–272.
36 Lary JM, Conover DL, Foley ED, Hanser PL: Teratogenic effects of 27 MHz radiofrequency radiation in rats. Teratology 1982;26:299–309.
37 Finnell RH, Moon SP, Abbott LC, Golden JA, Chernoff GF: Strain differences in heat-induced neural tube defects in mice. Teratology 1986;33: 241–252.
38 Hendrickx AG, Stone GW, Henrickson RV, Matayoshi K: Teratogenic effects of hyperthermia in bonnet monkeys (*Macaca radiata*). Teratology 1979;19:177–182.
39 Hoyme HE, Jones KL, van Allen MI, Saunders BS, Benirschke K: Vascular pathogenesis of transverse limb reduction defects. J Pediatr 1982; 101:839–843.
40 Van Allen MI, Hoyme HE, Jones KL: Vascular pathogenesis of limb defects. 1. Radial artery anatomy in radial aplasia. J Pediatr 1982;101: 832–838.
41 Fraser FC: Experimental teratogenesis in relation to congenital malformations in man; in Fishbein M (ed): Proc of the 2nd Int Conf on Congenital Malformations. New York, International Medical Congress, 1964, pp 277–287.
42 Lipson AH, Webster WS, Brown-Woodman PDC, Osborn RA: Moebius syndrome: Animal model – Human correlations and evidence for a brainstem vascular etiology. Teratology 1989;40:339–350.
43 McMurray RG, Katz VL: Thermoregulation in pregnancy: Implications for exercise. Sports Med 1990;10:146–158.
44 Jarski RW, Trippett DL: The risks and benefits of exercise during pregnancy. J Fam Pract 1990; 30:185–189.

Richard H. Finnell
Department of Veterinary Anatomy and Public Health
College of Veterinary Medicine
Texas A & M University
College Station, TX 77843 (USA)

Dev Brain Dysfunct 1993;6:210–228

1019–5815/93/0065–0210$2.75/0

Diabetes in Pregnancy as a Model for Testing Behavioural Teratogenicity in Man

E.J.H. Mulder

Department of Obstetrics and Gynaecology, University Hospital Utrecht, The Netherlands

Key Words. Behavioural teratology · Developmental disorders · Fetal movements · Behavioural states · Diabetes mellitus

Abstract. The existing knowledge on the functional development of the fetus' central nervous system (CNS) in uncomplicated pregnancy is summarized. It is advocated that the current techniques to study normal prenatal neurology are used for testing behavioural teratogenicity in man. Any substance potentially noxious to the CNS, should ideally be subjected to this method of testing. Such a study, though extensive and time-consuming, is feasible. This is shown using diabetes mellitus as an example. Maternal diabetes poses a risk to the developing fetus. The risk for structural malformations of the CNS is increased. Abnormal functional development of the fetal nervous system exists also in diabetic pregnancy, even when well controlled. Indicative of this are a delayed emergence of fetal movement patterns in the first trimester of pregnancy, altered regulation of fetal breathing movements, delayed and/or disturbed emergence of fetal behavioural states ('sleep-wake' cycles) in the third trimester and, in the neonatal period, continuity of poor behavioural state organization, immature EEG patterns and a high incidence of periodic breathing.

Introduction

Maternal type 1 (insulin-dependent) diabetes mellitus is associated with embryonic and fetal developmental disorders, both structural and functional. A number of these disorders concerns the central nervous system (CNS).

Diabetes mellitus is a complex metabolic and hormonal disease which brings about alterations in many body substances. In the light of this knowledge, the whole 'milieu' or assembly of substances in which the fetus is conceived and develops has to be considered to be the teratogen, rather than the traditional teratologists' definition of a specific substance (or its metabolites) being the culprit. Consequently, the concept of behavioural teratology has to be extended to include the potential effects of quantitatively or qualitatively altered mixtures of substances on the brain during CNS development [1].

In this paper, data on developmental disorders occurring in diabetic pregnancy are reviewed. Special emphasis is laid on the functional development of the CNS and on the techniques to study this during the embryonic and fetal periods. In fact, this paper describes techniques for fetal behavioural teratogenicity testing in general, with maternal diabetes as an example. Further, structural malformations and disturbances in the functional development of other fetal organs are briefly discussed, as well as animal experiments performed in order to analyze the pathogenesis of diabetes-related developmental disorders.

Behavioural Teratology

Many factors can underlie damage to the human CNS during development. These include teratogenic, genetic and iatrogenic factors, nutritional deficiencies, intoxications and fetal infections. Disorders of the CNS may originate any time from conception until late in infancy. Structural malformations are most likely induced before the tenth week of pregnancy and are usually apparent after delivery. Functional disorders of the CNS, however, may be recognizable immediately after birth, may emerge during subsequent development or may not become apparent until well after birth. Nevertheless, for many neurological dysfunctions the basis is laid during the prenatal period. If certain teratogenic agents are involved, it is essential to identify them, as well as to examine the mechanism by which they exert their deleterious effect and the extent of their noxiousness. This brings us to the domain of behavioural teratology, the study of substances that might cause functional deficits, including behavioural changes, following exposure during development in utero.

So far, the studies on recognized (alcohol, methyl mercury, lead [2]) and suspected behavioural teratogens in man (phenobarbital, opiates [2], diethylstilbestrol [3], clonidine [4]) were confined to the postnatal period, where interactions with the social environment may have interfered with the effects of drug exposure before birth. Thus, direct evidence obtained from observations during the prenatal period is the most reliable. Moreover, early assessment of the fetal neurological condition (judged as normal, suspect or abnormal) facilitates differentiation between pre-, peri- and postnatal injuries to the CNS.

For behavioural teratogenicity testing to be successful in human prenatal life, it requires [2]: (1) a technique to visualize and a method to classify and quantify fetal behaviour; (2) substantial data on appropriate control subjects, studied in an identical way; the normal variability and range of occurrence of fetal behaviour must be fully known; (3) a longitudinal study during which fetal behaviour is analyzed at different stages during development, starting as early as possible; (4) data from human epidemiological or case studies which suggest that the substance in question is a behavioural teratogen; (5) solid evidence that the substance is likely to affect CNS development (structural and/or functional) and, if possible, has demonstrable effects on brain receptors and biochemistry (e.g. neurotransmitters).

The ultimate goal of this type of research is to detect the effects of a particular substance (or its metabolites) on fetal behaviour and also to characterize these effects. Such studies have become possible since the introduction of dynamic imaging ultrasound. This technique has been designed to observe the fetus safely and directly in its natural environment and allows the accurate assessment of spontaneous human fetal behaviour under normal and abnormal circumstances.

Functional Development of the Fetal CNS in Normal Pregnancy

The non-invasive technique of real-time ultrasound imaging allows repeated and prolonged observations, providing a means of longitudinally investigating the emergence and differentiation of an individual's prenatal movement repertoire. As fetal movements are expressions of fetal CNS activity, their study allows the assessment of the functional development of the motor part of the CNS.

Emergence and Differentiation of Fetal Movements

Extensive investigations have provided detailed information on fetal motor development during the first and second half of normal pregnancy [5 – 8]. Briefly, the human fetus moves spontaneously in utero as early as 7 – 8 weeks of gestation and exhibits from that age onwards a set of specific movement patterns, such as startles, general movements, breathing movements, hiccups and isolated movements of the limbs and head. For each movement pattern, the age of first appearance in early development (7 – 20 weeks) has been established [5]. Fetal eye movements can first be seen between 16 and 19 weeks of gestation [9]. So, the 15- to 20-week-old fetus is capable of performing the whole motor repertoire of the neonate. An overview of the distinct fetal movement patterns is presented in figure 1.

Reports have appeared on developmental trends in the occurrence of these different movements during pregnancy, as well as figures on the variability and range of occurrence and on the intervals at which they are generated by the CNS [6 – 8]. It is noteworthy that there are large interindividual variations in the occurrence of the different movement patterns at all ages, resulting in wide ranges. Moreover, for body and breathing movements diurnal variations in occurrence exist from 20 weeks onwards [10, 11].

At the end of the second gestational trimester, cyclic changes can be observed in the incidences of fetal body and eye movements (rest-activity cycles), as well as in fetal heart rate variation. At that time, these three variables, the so-called fetal state variables, cycle more or less independently of one another, but they become progressively linked in the course of the third trimester of pregnancy. This results in fetal behavioural states which are fully developed after about 36 weeks [12 – 14].

Fetal Behavioural States

Behavioural states are distinct and discontinuous modes of neural activity. Four fetal states, two sleep and two awake states, have been defined, each by a specific combination of parameters of the three state variables [13].

State 1F ('quiet' sleep) is characterized by a stable heart rate with a small oscillation bandwidth (heart rate pattern A) and absence of eye and generalized body movements. In state 2 F ('active' sleep), eye movements and periodic general movements are present, and the fetal heart rate has a wide oscillation bandwidth between the frequent accelerations (pattern B). In state 3F ('quiet' awake), general

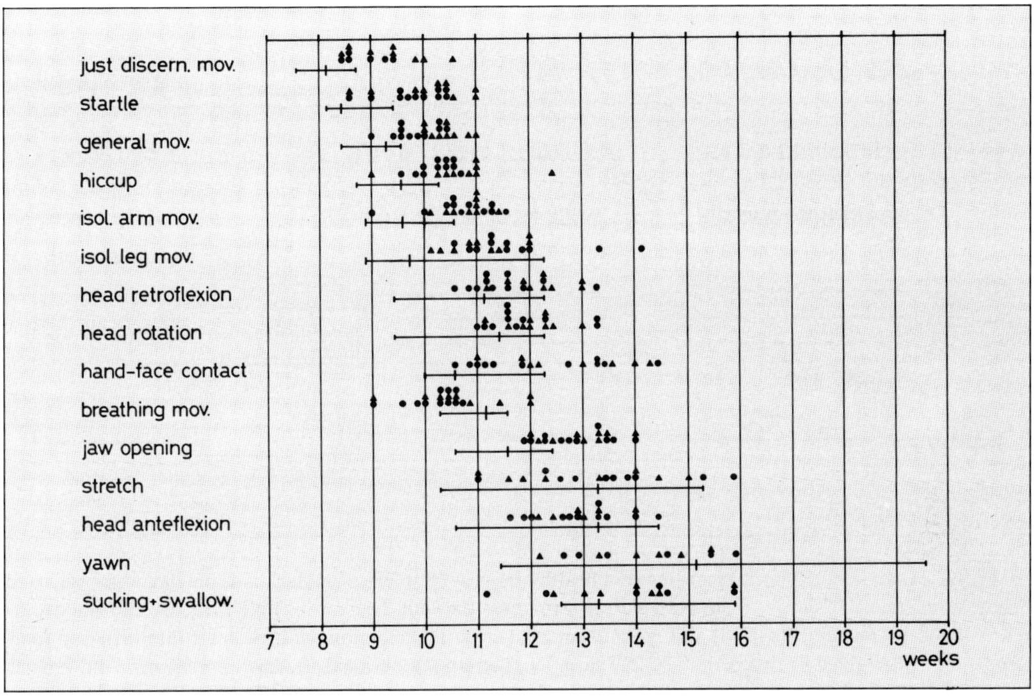

Fig. 1. Timetable of the emergence of specific fetal movement patterns in type 1 diabetic women as compared to control data (shown as medians and ranges). Each symbol represents the first occurrence of a particular pattern in an individual fetus studied longitudinally at weekly intervals. • = Preconceptional start of continuous subcutaneous insulin infusion, ▲ = start of continuous subcutaneous insulin infusion after conception. Ages at observation are given in full weeks and days.

movements are absent, eye movements are present and the fetal heart rate shows a wide oscillation bandwidth without accelerations (pattern C). In state 4F ('active' awake) there are prolonged accelerations (pattern D), almost continuous general movements and eye movements present. These fetal states correspond with states 1 – 4 in the full-term newborn infant [12].

Each state is relatively stable, i.e. is maintained uninterruptedly over longer periods (from a few minutes to more than an hour), and the transitions from one state into another are characterized by the almost simultaneous change of state variables, i.e. within 3 min. The site of the hypothetical generator of behavioural states is believed to be in the lower midbrain [15]. Both the building-up and the maintenance of a particular state require normal brain function. The presence of well-coordinated behavioural states (see fig. 2 for an example) is one of the indicators of maturity and integrity of the fetal nervous system.

The occurrence of the states 1F – 4F (percentage incidence and duration of enclosed state epochs) has been reported [13, 14, 16, 17]. Cycles of total sleep (a period of states 1F and 2F at a stretch) last for about 1 – 1.5 h.

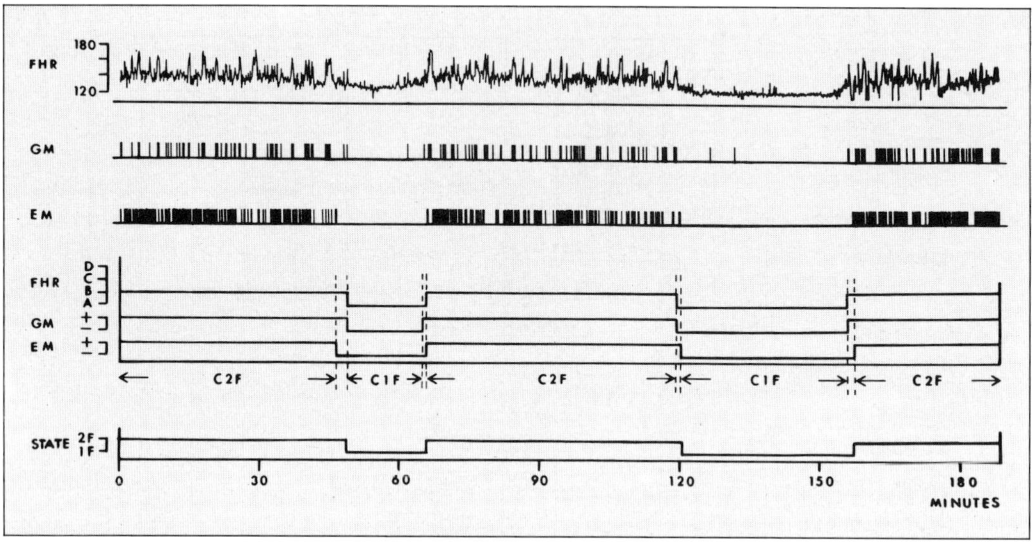

Fig. 2. Example of a 3-hour recording of a healthy fetus at 38 weeks of gestation displaying well-organized behavioural states. It shows, from above downwards: (**a**) the fetal heart rate (FHR) tracing and the occurrence of general movements (GM) and eye movements (EM). Three periods of high heart rate variation (pattern B) were interrupted by two periods of low variation (pattern A); during the former, both general movements and eye movements were present (2F combination) but absent during pattern A (1F combination); (**b**) profiles of the three state variables; (**c**) the presence of true behavioural states 1F and 2F with transitions lasting less than 3 min.

The occurrence of states 3F and 4F is usually low, except during the night-time.

Information is also available on the state-dependent quantity of fetal general movements and breathing movements. As regards the former, the percentage incidence, frequency and duration per burst have been presented for states 1F and 2F [17]. Breathing movements occur with a more regular rhythm in state 1F than in state 2F [18], but controversy exists as to the incidence of breathing. Some authors observed that fetuses breathe less during state 1F [16, 19], whereas others found no difference in incidence between the two states [17].

The organization of behavioural states in the human fetus is not easily influenced by maternal or environmental factors. Hitherto, it has been found that in normal pregnancy, state 1F is not influenced by Braxton Hicks' contractions [20] and uterine contractions during labour [21], nor by induced maternal emotions [22], shaking the maternal abdomen [23] and transabdominal sound stimulation [24, 25]. These findings are in line with the fact that it is difficult to wake up a newborn infant when in state 1 [12]. However, state 1F can be disturbed by a strong, inadequate stimulus which is probably nociceptive, as was found using vibro-acoustic stimulation with an artificial electronic larynx applied directly to the maternal abdomen [25].

Being able to study the integrity of fetal behavioural states may be considered as an important new tool in the identification of disturbances in the development of the fetal CNS and in testing behavioural teratogenicity in the human.

Functional Development of the Fetal CNS in Diabetic Pregnancy

What makes diabetes mellitus a good model for testing behavioural teratogenicity in man? In diabetic pregnancy, the fetal nervous system runs an increased risk of being malformed [26, 27], and its function has shown signs of impaired neurobehavioural development, demonstrable in the neonatal period [28, 29] and at school age [30 – 33]. Little is known about whether diabetes-related substances have any effect on fetal brain development. Insulin (of fetal origin), for instance, is not believed to promote brain growth [34]. However, evidence does exist that there are insulin-specific receptors in the brain and that these may be involved in neurotransmission and neuromodulation [35]. Therefore, it can be concluded that pregnancy in diabetic women is an appropriate model for testing behavioural teratogenicity, as it fulfils the requirements 4 and 5 (see above).

Until recently, behavioural studies performed on fetuses of diabetic women were almost non-existent. The few exceptions suggested delayed fetal neurological development [36, 37]. However, these studies had several disadvantages. They were cross-sectional, restricted to the third trimester of pregnancy, and fetal movements were not visualized ultrasonographically but recorded by the use of a mechanical device. This technique underestimates the total amount of fetal activity, and no information is obtained on which specific movement pattern has been recorded.

We investigated longitudinally the functional development of the CNS in fetuses of women with insulin-dependent diabetes [17, 38 – 41]. All the women were being treated with continuous subcutaneous insulin infusion therapy. Treatment was started either before conception or during the first months of pregnancy. The periconceptional quality of glycaemic control, as judged by the content of glycosylated haemoglobin, was generally better in the group of women who had been adjusted to an insulin pump before conception [38].

The study included behavioural observations obtained during an interval ranging from the embryonic period to the postnatal age of 1 week. Moreover, the infants of diabetic mothers (IDMs) were psychologically tested until the age of 4.5 years. The results of these investigations are summarized here. Study design and data analysis were identical to those employed in normal pregnancy [5 – 7, 13].

Emergence and Differentiation of Fetal Movements

All the types of motor activity observed in the embryos and fetuses of diabetic women could be classified in accordance with the movement patterns known from normal fetuses [39]. However, with the exception of breathing movements, there was a 1- to 2-week delay in the first appearance of all movement patterns which normally emerge during the first 12 weeks of pregnancy (fig. 1). Breathing movements were observed for the first time at an earlier age than in the control fetuses. This early emergence was all the more striking when their generally smaller size was taken into account.

When the emergence of frequently occurring movement patterns (the uppermost seven

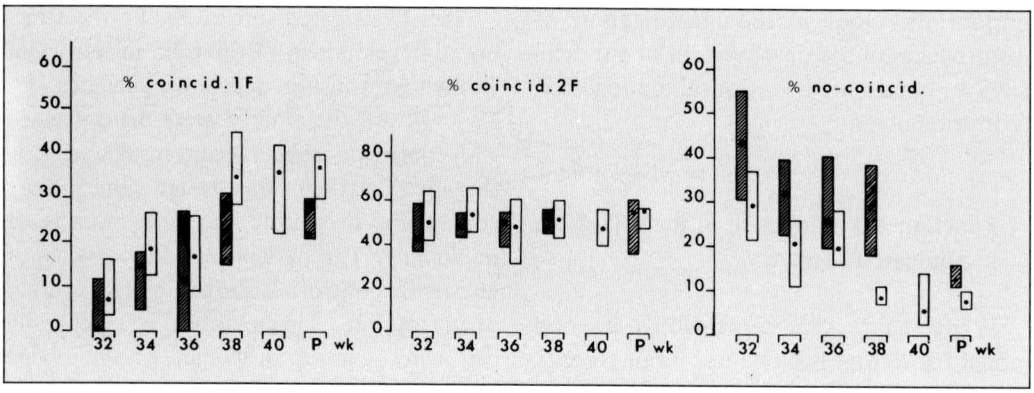

Fig. 3. Developmental course of 1F and 2F combinations and of no-coincidence (percentage of observation time) for fetuses of diabetic women (shaded bars) as compared to control values. Presented are the median and interquartile range at each studied age. P = Polygraphic recording at 1 week after birth.

in fig. 1) was plotted against fetal crown-rump length, which is usually smaller in diabetic pregnancy [38, 42, 43], there was still a general delay in comparison with the control group. The delay in motor development therefore does not run completely parallel with the delay in growth. This indicates the possible existence of a specific diabetes-related influence on the functional development of the embryonic and fetal nervous system. Hyperglycaemia, for example, may be responsible, as the delay in the emergence of fetal general movements was most profound in the women whose periconceptional glucose control was poor [39].

The developmental trends in the occurrence of all movement patterns (except startles) were similar to those seen in the control fetuses [40]. Due to delayed emergence, fetal movements occurred less frequently before 9 weeks of gestation, whereas after 12 weeks the overall incidence (total motor output) was higher than in the control group. The latter was mainly due to an increase in the incidence of fetal breathing movements. Breathing movements were generated differently by the CNS in the fetuses of diabetic women at the end of the first trimester. They occurred with longer intervals between two consecutive breaths, resulting in a slower rate. No relationship was found between the incidence of breathing movements at 12 – 16 weeks and the maternal blood glucose levels measured immediately prior to the recording.

The temporal patterning of other movement patterns, such as general movements and hiccups, did not differ between fetuses of the diabetic and control groups [40].

Behavioural States

In the fetuses of diabetic women, the emergence of behavioural states was delayed and/or disturbed in comparison with control fetuses [17, 41]. A low incidence of fetal quiescence (periods fitting the state 1F combination) appeared to be a common feature in diabetic pregnancy and has been found throughout the third trimester (fig. 3). This occurred especially in fetuses who were

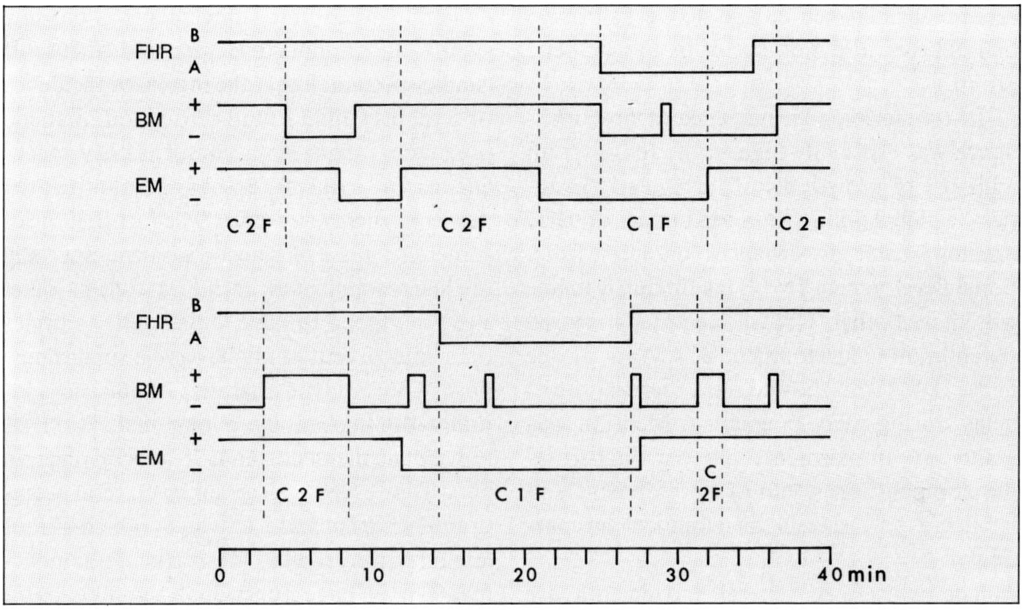

Fig. 4. Profiles of the three state variables at 32 weeks (**a**) and 38 weeks of gestation (**b**) in a fetus of a diabetic woman. At both 32 and 38 weeks the state variables cycled independently of one another. The expected, prolonged periods of stable association of the state variables did not occur at 38 weeks (see fig. 2) and behavioural states could not be identified. Periods that fit the 1F or 2F combinations (C1F, C2F) are indicated; the remainder is called no-coincidence. FHR = Fetal heart rate; BM = body movements; EM = eye movements.

macrosomic at birth. The progressive linkage of the three state variables, known from normally developing fetuses, rarely occurred during the third trimester of diabetic pregnancy (fig. 4). The criteria of true states were met in only 3 out of the 10 fetuses studied at 38 weeks of pregnancy [17]. This was due to a large number of asynchronous transitions (lasting more than 3 min) and to frequent interruption of the expected concordant association between the state 2F parameters. The result was a high occurrence of periods of 'no-coincidence' (fig. 3, 4), i.e. periods which could not be classified as either state 1F, 2F, 3F or 4F. No-coincidence may arise, for instance, if general movements occur in the presence of heart rate pattern B but without simultaneously occurring eye movements. This set of state parameters does not fit the defined state 2F combination. The incidence of no-coincidence may be regarded as a measure of organizational chaos.

These results suggest delayed and/or disturbed development of fetal brain function in diabetic pregnancies. The same conclusion was drawn by others [36] who investigated active and quiet periods of fetal motility (based on body movements and long-term heart rate variation only). They found that the doubling of the duration of these periods which takes place between 28 and 40 weeks in normal fetuses, did not occur in the diabetic group.

In our series, the incidence of no-coincidence was especially high in the fetuses with a history of growth delay during early gestation, which demonstrates the impact of early developmental disturbances on later functional development [44]. This finding is in line with that of others [45] who reported impaired psychomotor development at 4 years of age in the IDMs who showed intra-uterine growth delay during early pregnancy. Mention was made of impairments in personal-social development, gross motor development and language and speech development in particular.

The way fetal general movements are generated by the CNS did not differ between the fetuses of the diabetic and control groups [17], which was also described for the first trimester [40]. In contrast, the analysis of breathing movements at 38 weeks of pregnancy revealed altered neural regulation in the fetuses of diabetic women [17]. As described for the first trimester, breathing movements were more numerous but occurred at a considerably slower rate than in the control fetuses. Apparently, diabetes has an effect on fetal breathing, and the influence is present from the onset of these movements onwards.

In normal pregnancy, fetal breathing activity is related to maternal plasma glucose concentration [10, 46]. However, the underlying mechanism in diabetic pregnancy might be different, since no clear relationship was found between the breathing incidence and the actual glucose level either in the first [40] or in the third trimester [47]. Moreover, glucose has no effect on the breath-to-breath interval in non-diabetic pregnancy and, hence, does not alter the rate of breathing [46].

Fetal breathing movements consume significant amounts of oxygen and glucose. It can be speculated that the increased incidence of fetal breathing found throughout diabetic pregnancy might be a compensatory mechanism for reducing excessive quantities of delivered energy substrate. The fact that third-trimester fetuses of diabetic women, especially the macrosomic ones, spend less time in 'quiet sleep' and tend to have longer activity cycles than control fetuses might serve a similar purpose. Thus, maybe an excess of glucose is initially diminished by a maximalization of movement incidence and, if hyperglycaemia persists or exceeds a certain level, fetal accretion mechanisms are activated, which stimulate fetal overgrowth [44]. If true, fetal movements may have functional significance in three distinct ways. Firstly, some movement patterns are of importance to the instantaneous survival or behavioural and morphological development of the fetus. Secondly, other movements prepare the fetus by practice and exercise for his or her postnatal life. Thirdly, as moving costs energy, fetal motility may regulate the flow of energy.

Infants of Women with Diabetes

Poor organization of behavioural states, as reflected by a high incidence of no-coincidence (fig. 3), was also present at 1 week after birth and must therefore be considered as a sequel of long-term exposure to the non-optimal intra-uterine environment, as is present in diabetic gravidae [17].

The EEG patterns obtained in the neonates of diabetic women were generally judged as quite immature. Moreover, periodic breathing occurred much more often during state 2 in the newborns of the diabetic group than in control infants (on average 14 and 2%, respectively). The higher incidence of periodic breathing in the IDMs reflects less stability in control of the respiratory system. This is probably due to immaturity of the neural mechanisms underlying respiration, as suggested by the fact that the amount of periodic breathing decreased with age in control infants, but not in IDMs [17].

The poor behavioural state organization in the diabetic group, both before and after birth, resembles more immature patterns. The observed immature EEG patterns and the high incidence of periodic breathing in IDMs corroborate the same conclusion.

Still other evidence of delayed cerebral maturation are the increased levels of α-melanocyte-stimulating hormone found in the cord blood of newborns of diabetic women [48]. The protein α-melanocyte-stimulating hormone is produced by the pars intermedia of the fetal pituitary which regresses with increasing age during normal third-trimester development. The higher levels of α-melanocyte-stimulating hormone may therefore reflect a delay in the regression of the pars intermedia. The observations made over 20 years ago by Schulte et al. [28, 49, 50] are in accordance with the former results. They studied behavioural states in newborn IDMs and found several immature characteristics of sleep [28]. Their EEG patterns resembled those of less mature normal infants, i.e. of 36 weeks or younger [49]. The neurological condition of the IDMs was often judged as hyperexcitable [50]. Others, investigating IDMs during the first week of life, found marked differences in behaviour in comparison with control infants. In IDMs, there was a higher incidence of neurological disorders, mainly caused by hypotonia [51]. Furthermore, IDMs scored lower on the Brazelton scale on days 3, 5 and 7, comprising items on motor performance, sensory orientation and autonomic stability [29].

Controversy exists as to whether these differences in newborns persist and influence their later development. In our series, later development appeared to be favourable. A follow-up study was carried out on 40 IDMs, including a number of the infants studied in utero [52]. The IDMs were investigated at various ages between 10 months and 4.5 years of age using a set of different psychological tests appropriate for the age at examination (e.g. Bayley test between 10 and 30 months). Assessment was made of the level of mental, speech, motor, temperament and behavioural development. These aspects of neuropsychological development did not differ between the IDMs and a group of matched control infants. When a subgroup of IDMs with a high birth weight was analyzed separately, one difference was found: a delay in motor development in comparison with the control infants with a high or normal birth weight. It therefore seems that, generally, IDMs developed successfully after birth. This is in line with the conclusion drawn by others who found no impairment of the intellectual status of IDMs at the age of 5 years [53], 7 years [54] or at other ages [55]. Nevertheless, infants with a history of early embryonic/fetal growth delay [44, 45] or those who are macrosomic at birth [52] continue to run an increased risk.

Studies on neurological and psychomotor development in IDMs which were carried out before 1980, generally indicated a poor prognosis for these infants. Long-term effects on the development of IDMs were shown, reflected by low intellectual performance at the age of 4 years [30] and a moderate [31] or high incidence [32, 33] of cerebral dysfunction. The improvements made during the past decennium may be due to better blood glucose control during pregnancy and/or to better obstetrical and neonatal management.

Functional Development of Other Fetal Organ Systems in Diabetic Pregnancy

A delay in the functional development of the placenta and various fetal organs has also been described in diabetic pregnancy, although the literature is scant of reports.

Evidence was found for delayed early placentation, as judged from placental lactogen concentrations [56]. Placental abnormalities seen after diabetic pregnancy generally represent immature characteristics of development; the degree of 'immaturity' does not appear to be related to the quality of glucose control [57].

A delay in the development of the fetal liver has been suggested on the basis of low α-fetoprotein levels in maternal serum in early pregnancy [27, 58] and on high levels in cord blood at delivery [59]. The increased incidence of neonatal hyperbilirubinaemia has also been ascribed to the relative immaturity of the liver [60].

Best documented is the delayed (biochemical) maturation of the fetal lung [61]. It involves a delay in the production of surfactant and its constituents. The deficiency of pulmonary surfactant may result in the respiratory distress syndrome.

Behavioural Teratology: An Outlook

The functional development of the fetal CNS during diabetic pregnancy differed from that observed in normal pregnancy. CNS-related functions showed delayed and/or disturbed characteristics. Indicative of this were the delayed emergence of movement patterns in the first trimester of pregnancy, the delayed emergence of behavioural states in the third trimester and, after birth, the continuity of poor behavioural state organization, immature EEG patterns and a high incidence of periodic breathing. Evidence of delayed functional development of other fetal organs (the lung, liver and placenta) is in accordance with the findings on cerebral maturation in fetuses and newborn infants of diabetic women. Of special interest was the observation that embryos and fetuses who were smaller than normal during early diabetic pregnancy exhibited the poorest organization of behavioural states near term. These results not only demonstrate the feasibility of testing behavioural teratogenicity in man, but also the possibility to detect effects of diabetes on fetal behaviour and to characterize these effects.

The existing knowledge on fetal movements and behavioural states forms the essential basis for any comparative study. In theory, any substance displaying recognized or suspected evidence of CNS toxicity in humans should be subjected to the method of testing behavioural teratogenicity.

Possible functional aberrations of the normal developmental course may be: altered output of motor activity in general – reduction in the number of distinct movement patterns, the occurrence of movements which cannot be classified as one of the predefined patterns, extremely low or high occurrence rate, change of temporal patterning, change in the quality of motor performance – or the dissociation of state parameters which results in poorly established behavioural states near term [12, 62].

At present, there is increasing evidence that

for many years, the decline in the incidence of severe neurological disorders kept pace with the decrease in perinatal deaths. However, during the past decennium, the latter have continued to fall, whereas the incidence of neurological disorders (cerebral palsy) has increased [63, 64]. The reasons for the increase in handicaps are obscure, but if they are related to environmental agents and have their origin before birth, it is very important to possess a record of the fetal neurological condition. This way, the possible effect of serious intra-uterine injuries on brain development is probably easier to unravel from the consequences of peri- and postnatal complications. Such knowledge might be of great help in the interpretation of the results of psychoneurological follow-up studies.

Fetal Structural Malformations

Pregnancy in women with diabetes is often associated with structural developmental disorders of the CNS, cardiovascular system, urogenital tract and the skeleton. The rate of occurrence of these malformations is 6 – 12%, i.e. they are 2 – 4 times more frequent in IDMs than in infants of non-diabetic mothers [26, 65]. The rate of neural-tube defects has been reported to be 3 – 20 times that in the general population [26, 27].

Recent studies emphasized the importance of establishing and maintaining (near) normal glucose profiles in diabetic women before conception, during organogenesis and for the entire duration of pregnancy [66, 67]. However, in a large prospective multicentre study, Mills et al. [68] did not find a significant correlation between hypoglycaemic events, glycosylated haemoglobin content or mean blood glucose levels in early pregnancy and the occurrence of malformations in the offspring of diabetic women. As the authors pointed out, only glycaemic factors were examined, which leaves open the possibility that other teratogens were involved.

Some specialized centres have reported a decrease to the normal base rate of malformations by placing the diabetic women under tight metabolic control and close medical supervision before conception and thereafter [69 – 71]. However, one should realize that many diabetic women are late-entry patients and/or visit a less well-equipped hospital; therefore they still face a high malformation rate. In addition, the existence of a clear cause-effect relationship between (near) normoglycaemia and the reduction in fetal malformations has not been fully proved [68].

Early Embryonic/Fetal Growth Delay

Pedersen and Mølsted-Pedersen [42] first made the observation that many embryos and fetuses of type 1 diabetic women are smaller than controls (as judged by the crown-rump length) between 7 and 14 weeks of pregnancy. This phenomenon, called early growth delay, has been found both in cross-sectional studies [42, 58, 72] and in a longitudinal study [38]. The most profound delay in embryonic and fetal size occurred in women with elevated glycosylated haemoglobin values during the early weeks of pregnancy [43]. In these cases, with poorly controlled maternal glucose levels, the incidence of malformations [70, 73] and (possibly) of spontaneous abortion [74] was also high.

The somatic growth delay is accompanied by a delay in placental development [56]. Growth delay detected in early pregnancy has been related to poor fetal behavioural state organization [44] and to low intellectual performance at the age of 4 years [45].

To date, it is unknown whether a common mechanism underlies early growth delay and other developmental aberrations or whether it is possible that these phenomena and the metabolic status of the pregnant diabetic patient are merely coexistent without any cause-effect relationship.

There are various theoretical explanations for the smaller size of the embryos in diabetic pregnancy: delayed ovulation, delayed conception, delayed implantation, impaired development of the yolk sac, a temporary arrest of embryonic growth during organogenesis and slow embryonic growth rate. It is as yet unknown which of these processes is/are at work in women with diabetes. Intrafollicular overripeness of the ovum and delayed ovulation are common in diabetic women, especially in those with poor glucose control [75]. It has been claimed that early growth delay is solely due to late ovulation [76]. Late conception is an unlikely explanation, but delayed implantation is well documented in man [77]. The postimplantation events are also likely to be involved.

Macrosomia

The development of macrosomia (birth weight >90th centile) is generally believed to be a third-trimester phenomenon, as no signs of head-to-body disproportion were found prior to 30 weeks of pregnancy [78]. However, recently it has been found that in some diabetic cases, fetal macrosomia develops from an early stage in pregnancy (16–22 weeks). There is evidence now of two or three markedly different intra-uterine growth patterns [38, 79, 80].

Fetal macrosomia is still more common (2–3 times) in diabetic than in normal pregnancy, despite tight maternal glucose control during the entire duration of pregnancy. The most frequently mentioned incidence of macrosomia ranges between 25 and 30% [81, 82]. This figure is not very different from the rate of macrosomia (32%) as calculated over the period from 1956 to 1978 [83]. Therefore, the classical maternal hyperglycaemia-fetal hyperinsulinaemia hypothesis falls short as the sole explanation for macrosomia. Elevated concentrations of other nutrients, such as amino acids and triglycerides, may also stimulate the hypersecretion of fetal insulin, even in the presence of normal glucose levels [1, 79, 80]. In addition, others have suggested that, apart from insulin, placental and/or other fetal hormones may also have growth-promoting potency, e.g. prolactin, placental lactogen, chorionic gonadotropin and the insulin-like growth factors 1 and 2 (somatomedins) [84]. To date, however, their effects and way of action are not fully understood. Further, it is possible that fetal insulin production and release are controlled, as in the adult, by the CNS via a complex feedback system [85]. Macrosomia may, like obesity, develop as a result of neuro-endocrine dysfunction.

Animal Studies on Diabetes-Related Developmental Disorders

In numerous experimental rodent studies, both in vivo and in vitro, impairment of embryonic growth and differentiation has been demonstrated under diabetes-related conditions. Fetal functional development, however, has not been studied in rodents to date.

In Vivo Experiments

In vivo studies have demonstrated the common occurrence of fetal growth delay (the young were smaller and weighed less than normal at birth) and induction of malformation in rats when pregnancy was complicated by naturally occurring or drug-induced maternal diabetes [86, 87]. More precisely, impairment of growth in vivo occurred during early embryogenesis in diabetic rats, i.e. before day 11.5 of gestational age (the total duration of rat gestation is 20 days) when the placenta is not yet fully operative [87]. At that stage, the embryos showed a smaller crown-rump length, a smaller number of somites and less DNA/embryo and were often malformed. The hyperglycaemic state of the animals was implicated as a potential growth-inhibitory and teratogenic factor. Hypoglycaemia has the same effects in vivo; even a 1 hour period of maternal hypoglycaemia during early organogenesis (day 9.5) in the non-diabetic rat resulted in general growth delay and gross anomalies in the embryos when examined 2 days later [88]. Experimentally produced fetal macrosomia is considered to be an exception in diabetic rodents [86] but has been studied successfully in the fetal monkey [34].

In Vitro Experiments

The technique of whole-embryo culture has been employed on a large scale to study diabetic embryopathy. It involves the culture of postimplantation rodent embryos during their critical period of organogenesis (24 – 48 h) and resembles what happens in the third to sixth gestational weeks in human embryos. This method allows the assessment of individual teratogens and the concentrations at which they exert their deleterious action [89, 90].

A multitude of diabetes-related factors was found to be growth-inhibitory and teratogenic, usually inducing neural-tube defects ('exencephaly'). These include hyperglycaemia, hypoglycaemia, ketone bodies, deficiency of trace elements (zinc and manganese) and tissue homogenates of placenta and decidua [89, 90]. It should be emphasized that these experiments are relatively acute perturbations and that the adverse effects were observed under conditions of extreme deficiency or excess of the studied compound. The concentration of glucose, for instance, varied between 0.3 – 0.5 (hypoglycaemia) and 4 – 10 (hyperglycaemia) times the normal level. Methodological differences also play a role. The serum may be 'pure' (i.e. withdrawn from a diabetic or normal animal), pooled, diluted, insulin-induced hypoglycaemic or enriched by exogenous supplement.

The use of undiluted human serum for whole-embryo culture therefore has obvious benefits. The main advantage is probably the direct exposure of embryos and their extra-embryonic membranes to a total 'milieu' with concentrations of substances and metabolites that occur under (patho)physiological circumstances in man. When we used this technique with human diabetic serum, we saw no sign of impaired growth or differentiation in cultured rat embryos, nor did we find any clue for a potential teratogenic factor [91]. The question therefore remains: Which of the factors with known effects in other experiments should be incriminated in the human? Hypoglycaemia seems to be the most unlikely candidate, as was reassured by an extensive clinical study [68]. Hyperglycaemia, on the other hand, is generally accepted as the most plausible causative factor among the metabolic disturbances present in early pregnancy. It is not clear by which mechanism and biochemical mediators elevated glucose levels exert the adverse influence during organogenesis. Several modes of action have been suggested for hyperglycaemia: disruption of glycolysis, inhibition of mitosis, inhibition of somatomedin action and inhibition of prostaglandin metabolism by causing deficiency of arachidonic acid and/or myo-inositol [89–92].

It is open to debate whether hyperglycaemia acts solely or whether its effect also depends on or interacts (via synergism) with other metabolic factors; embryopathy in diabetic pregnancy may be of multifactorial origin [90, 93]. Further, substantial evidence was found that the yolk sac plays an integral role in diabetic embryopathy [92, 94].

Recently, attention was directed to the preimplantation period of development, i.e. the time from fertilization to implantation, which lasts for about 7 days in humans. High glucose and insulin levels have been shown to adversely affect the morphological development (inner cell mass) of pre-implantation rodent embryos [95, 96]. In vivo, these early injuries may have subsequent expression in later stages of development, such as growth delay and/or malformations. The early embryos seem to exhibit differential sensitivity to treatment dependent on a specific developmental stage (morula, blastocyst) [96].

Concluding Remarks

Pregnancy is no longer a perilous experiment for a woman with diabetes. Most diabetic women can conceive and give birth to a baby nowadays, although the risk of a number of complications is still several times that seen in the general population. The data reviewed here showed that maternal diabetes is associated with embryonic and fetal developmental disorders, both structural and functional. These include an increased incidence of structural malformations, early growth delay, late macrosomia and disturbances in the functional development of the placenta and of fetal organ systems, such as the liver, lungs and CNS. Some could be related to the quality of maternal glucose control, while for others, such a relationship was less clear.

From our own series, for instance, it appeared that tight glucose control of the mother is no guarantee that developmental disorders will be prevented. Adequate glucose control is not necessarily identical to adequate 'metabolic' control, and it may well be that other disturbances (e.g. of amino acids, free fatty acids) persist despite (near) normoglycaemia.

Nevertheless, good glucose control set up well in advance of conception is recommended by everyone, as it is virtually the only remedy at the moment [68].

Acknowledgment

The author wishes to express his gratitude to Prof. Dr. G.H.A. Visser for critically reading the manuscript.

References

1 Freinkel N: Of pregnancy and progeny. Diabetes 1980;29:1023–1035.
2 Anonymous: WHO Guidelines for the Assessment of Drugs and Other Chemicals for Behavioural Teratogenicity. Copenhagen, World Health Organization regional office for Europe, 1986.
3 Ehrhardt AA, Meyer-Bahlburg HFL: The effects of prenatal diethylstilbestrol (DES) on female adult behavior. Teratology 1990;42:13A.
4 Huisjes HJ, Hadders-Algra M, Touwen BCL: Is clonidine a behavioural teratogen in the human? Early Hum Dev 1986;14:43–48.

5 de Vries JIP, Visser GHA, Prechtl HFR: The emergence of fetal behaviour. I. Qualitative aspects. Early Hum Dev 1982;7:301 – 322.

6 de Vries JIP, Visser GHA, Prechtl HFR: The emergence of fetal behaviour. II. Quantitative aspects. Early Hum Dev 1985;12:99 – 120.

7 de Vries JIP, Visser GHA, Prechtl HFR: The emergence of fetal behaviour. III. Individual differences and consistencies. Early Hum Dev 1988; 16:85 – 103.

8 Roodenburg PJ, Wladimiroff JW, van Es A, Prechtl HFR: Classification and quantitative aspects of fetal movements during the second half of normal pregnancy. Early Hum Dev 1991;25: 19 – 35.

9 Birnholz JC: The development of human fetal eye movement patterns. Science 1981;213:679 – 681.

10 de Vries JIP, Visser GHA, Mulder EJH, Prechtl HFR: Diurnal and other variations in fetal movement and heart rate patterns at 20 – 22 weeks. Early Hum Dev 1987;15:333 – 348.

11 Patrick J, Campbell K, Carmichael L, Natale R, Richardson B: Patterns of gross fetal body movements over 24-hour observation intervals during the last 10 weeks of pregnancy. Am J Obstet Gynecol 1982;142:363 – 371.

12 Visser GHA, Prechtl HFR: Movements and behavioural states in the human fetus; in Jones CT (ed): Fetal and Neonatal Development. Ithaca, Perinatology Press, 1988, pp 581 – 590.

13 Nijhuis JG, Prechtl HFR, Martin CB, Bots RSGM: Are there behavioural states in the human fetus? Early Hum Dev 1982;6:177 – 195.

14 van Vliet MAT, Martin CB, Nijhuis JG, Prechtl HFR: Behavioural states in the fetuses of nulliparous women. Early Hum Dev 1985;12:121 – 135.

15 Dawes GS: The central nervous control of fetal behaviour. Eur J Obstet Gynecol Reprod Biol 1986;21:341 – 346.

16 Arduini D, Rizzo G, Giorlandino C, Valensise H, Dell'Acqua S, Romanini C: The development of fetal behavioural states: A longitudinal study. Prenat Diagn 1986;6:117 – 124.

17 Mulder EJH, O'Brien MJ, Lems YL, Visser GHA, Prechtl HFR: Body and breathing movements in near-term fetuses and newborn infants of type-1 diabetic women. Early Hum Dev 1990;24: 131 – 152.

18 Nijhuis JG, Martin CB, Gommers S, Bouws P, Bots RSGM, Jongsma HW: The rhythmicity of fetal breathing varies with behavioural state in the human fetus. Early Hum Dev 1983;9:1 – 7.

19 van Vliet MAT, Martin CB, Nijhuis JG, Prechtl HFR: The relationship between fetal activity and behavioural states and fetal breathing movements in normal and growth-retarded fetuses. Am J Obstet Gynecol 1985;153:582 – 588.

20 Mulder EJH, Visser GHA: Braxton Hicks' contractions and motor behaviour in the near-term human fetus. Am J Obstet Gynecol 1987;156: 543 – 549.

21 Griffin RL, Caron FJM, van Geijn HP: Behavioral states in the human fetus during labor. Am J Obstet Gynecol 1985;152:828 – 833.

22 Van den Bergh BRH, Mulder EJH, Visser GHA, Poelmann-Weesjes G, Bekedam DJ, Prechtl HFR: The effect of (induced) maternal emotions on fetal behaviour: A controlled study. Early Hum Dev 1989;19;9 – 19.

23 Visser GHA, Zeelenberg HJ, de Vries JIP, Dawes GS: External physical stimulation of the human fetus during episodes of low heart rate variation. Am J Obstet Gynecol 1983;145:579 – 584.

24 Schmidt W, Boos R, Gnirs J, Auer L, Schulze S: Fetal behavioural states and controlled sound stimulation. Early Hum Dev 1985;12:145 – 153.

25 Visser GHA, Mulder HH, Wit HP, Mulder EJH, Prechtl HFR: Vibro-acoustic stimulation of the human fetus: Effect on behavioural state organization. Early Hum Dev 1989;19:285 – 296.

26 Mills JL: Malformations in infants of diabetic mothers. Teratology 1982;25:385 – 394.

27 Milunsky A, Alpert E, Kitzmiller JL, Younger MD, Neff RK: Prenatal diagnosis of neural tube defects. VIII. The importance of serum alphafetoprotein screening in diabetic pregnant women. Am J Obstet Gynecol 1982;142:1030 – 1032.

28 Schulte FJ, Lasson U, Parl U, Nolte R, Jürgens U: Brain and behavioural maturation in newborn infants of diabetic mothers. II. Sleep cycles. Neuropädiatrie 1969;1:36 – 43.

29 Yogman MW, Cole P, Als H, Lester BM: Behavior of newborns of diabetic mothers. Infant Behav Dev 1982;5:331 – 340.

30 Churchill JA, Berendes HW, Nemore J: Neuropsychological deficits in children of diabetic mothers. Am J Obstet Gynecol 1969;105:257 – 268.

31 Stehbens JA, Baker GL, Kitchell M: Outcome at ages 1, 3, and 5 years of children born to diabetic women. Am J Obstet Gynecol 1977;127:408 – 413.

32 Bibergeil H, Gödel E, Amendt P: Diabetes and pregnancy: Early and late prognoses of children of diabetic mothers; in Camerini-Davalos RA, Cole HS (eds): Early Diabetes in Early Life. New York, Academic Press, 1975, pp 427 – 434.
33 Yssing M: Long-term prognosis of children born to mothers diabetic when pregnant; in Camerini-Davalos RA, Cole HS (eds): Early Diabetes in Early Life. New York, Academic Press, 1975, pp 575 – 586.
34 Susa JB: Effects of diabetes on fetal growth; in Reece EA, Coustan DR (eds): Diabetes Mellitus in Pregnancy. Principles and Practice. New York, Churchill Livingstone, 1988, pp 105 – 121.
35 Raizada MK, Shemer J, Judkins JH, Clarke DW, Masters BA, LeRoith D: Insulin receptors in the brain: Structural and physiological characterization. Neurochem Res 1988;4:297 – 303.
36 Dierker LJ, Pillay S, Sorokin Y, Rosen MG: The change in fetal activity periods in diabetic and nondiabetic pregnancies. Am J Obstet Gynecol 1982; 143:181 – 185.
37 Robertson SS, Dierker LJ: The development of cyclic motility in fetuses of diabetic mothers. Dev Psychobiol 1986;19:223 – 234.
38 Mulder EJH, Visser GHA: Growth and motor development in fetuses of women with type-1 diabetes. I. Early growth patterns. Early Hum Dev 1991;25:91 – 106.
39 Mulder EJH, Visser GHA: Growth and motor development in fetuses of women with type-1 diabetes. II. Emergence of specific movement patterns. Early Hum Dev 1991;25:107 – 115.
40 Mulder EJH, Visser GHA, Morssink LP, de Vries JIP: Growth and motor development in fetuses of women with type-1 diabetes. III. First trimester quantity of fetal movement patterns. Early Hum Dev 1991;25:117 – 133.
41 Mulder EJH; Visser GHA, Bekedam DJ, Prechtl HFR: Emergence of behavioural states in fetuses of type-1 diabetic women. Early Hum Dev 1987; 15:231 – 252.
42 Pedersen JF, Mølsted-Pedersen L: Early growth retardation in diabetic pregnancy. Br Med J 1979; i:18 – 19.
43 Pedersen JF, Mølsted-Pedersen L, Mortensen HB: Fetal growth delay and maternal hemoglobin A1c in early diabetic pregnancy. Obstet Gynecol 1984; 64:351 – 352.
44 Mulder EJH: Fetal Behaviour: Studies on Normal and Diabetic Pregnancy; PhD thesis University Groningen, 1990.
45 Bloch Petersen M, Pedersen SA, Greisen G, Pedersen JF, Mølsted-Pedersen L: Early growth delay in diabetic pregnancy: Relation to psychomotor development at age 4. Br Med J 1988;296: 598 – 600.
46 Adamson SL, Bocking A, Cousin AJ, Rapoport I, Patrick JE: Ultrasonic measurement of rate and depth of human fetal breathing: Effect of glucose. Am J Obstet Gynecol 1983;147:288 – 295.
47 Wladimiroff JW, Roodenburg PJ: Human fetal breathing and gross body activity relative to maternal meals during insulin-dependent pregnancy. Acta Obstet Gynecol Scand 1982;61:65 – 68.
48 Hassan MM, Bottoms SF, Evans MI, Dombrowski MP, Mariona FG, Mukherjee AB: Fetal α-melanocyte-stimulating hormone levels: No correlation with late fetal growth but increased with diabetes mellitus. Am J Obstet Gynecol 1986;154: 428 – 430.
49 Schulte FJ, Michaelis R, Nolte R, Albert G, Parl U, Lasson U: Brain and behavioural maturation in newborn infants of diabetic mothers. I. Nerve conduction and EEG patterns. Neuropädiatrie 1969;1:24 – 35.
50 Schulte FJ, Albert G, Michaelis R: Brain and behavioural maturation in newborn infants of diabetic mothers. III. Motor behaviour. Neuropädiatrie 1969;1:44 – 55.
51 Priestly BL: Neurological assessment of infants of diabetic mothers in the first week of life. Pediatrics 1972;50:578 – 583.
52 Holwerda-Kuipers J, Visser GHA: Psychological development of infants of women with type-1 diabetes; in: Proceedings of the 27th Meeting of the Dutch Federation of Medical Scientific Societies, Groningen, The Netherlands. Nijmegen, Federatie van Medisch Wetenschappelijke Verenigingen, 1986, p A171.
53 Persson B, Gentz J: Follow-up of children of insulin-dependent and gestational diabetic mothers. Neuropsychological outcome. Acta Paediatr Scand 1984;73:349 – 358.
54 Cummins M, Norrish M: Follow-up of children of diabetic mothers. Arch Dis Child 1980;55: 259 – 264.
55 Hadden DR, Byrne E, Trotter I, Harley JMG, McClure G, McAuley RR: Physical and psychological health of children of type 1 (insulin-

dependent) diabetic mothers. Diabetologia 1984; 26:250 – 254.

56 Pedersen JF, Mølsted-Pedersen L, Lebech PE: Is the early growth delay in the diabetic pregnancy accompanied by a delay in placental development? Acta Obstet Gynecol Scand 1986;65:675 – 677.

57 Laurini RN, Visser GHA, van Ballegooie E, Schoots CJF: Morphological findings in placentas of insulin-dependent diabetic patients treated with continuous subcutaneous insulin infusion (CSII). Placenta 1987;8:153 – 165.

58 Martin AO, Dempsey LM, Minogue J, Liu K, Keller J, Tamura R, Freinkel N: Maternal serum alpha-fetoprotein levels in pregnancies complicated by diabetes: Implications for screening programs. Am J Obstet Gynecol 1990;163:1209 – 1216.

59 Cuckle HS, Wald NJ, Hughes DR: Cord serum alpha-fetoprotein and maternal insulin-dependent diabetes mellitus. Br J Obstet Gynaecol 1989;96: 1450 – 1452.

60 Taylor PM, Wofson JH, Bright NH: Hyperbilirubinaemia in infants of diabetic mothers. Biol Neonate 1963;5:289 – 293.

61 Bourbon JR, Farrell PM: Fetal lung development in the diabetic pregnancy. Pediatr Res 1985;19: 253 – 267.

62 Prechtl HFR. Qualitative changes of spontaneous movements in fetus and preterm infant are a marker of neurological dysfunction. Early Hum Dev 1990;23:151 – 158.

63 Hagberg B, Hagberg G: The changing panorama of infantile hydrocephalus and cerebral palsy over forty years: A Swedish survey. Brain Dev 1989;11: 368 – 373.

64 Patel N (ed): Antenatal and Perinatal Causes of Handicap. Baillière's Clin Obstet Gynaecol. London, Baillière Tindall, 1988, vol 2/1.

65 Cowett RM, Schwartz R: The infant of the diabetic mother. Pediatr Clin North Am 1982;29: 1213 – 1231.

66 Key TC, Giuffrida R, Moore TR: Predictive value of early pregnancy glycohemoglobin in the insulin-treated diabetic patient. Am J Obstet Gynecol 1987;112:213 – 220.

67 Ylinen K, Aula P, Stenman UH, Kesäniemi-Kuokkanen T, Teramo K: Risk of minor and major fetal malformations in diabetics with high haemoglobin A1c values in early pregnancy. Br Med J 1984;289:345 – 346.

68 Mills JL, Knopp RH, Simpson JL, Jovanovic-Peterson L, Metzger BE, Holmes LB, Aarons JH, Brown Z, Reed GF, Bieber FR, Van Allen M, Holzman I, Ober C, Peterson CM, Withiam MJ, Duckles A, Mueller-Heubach E, Polk BF, the NICHD-Diabetes in Early Pregnancy Study: Lack of relation of increased malformation rates in infants of diabetic mothers to glycemic control during organogenesis. N Engl J Med 1988;318: 671 – 676.

69 Damm P, Mølsted-Pedersen L: Significant decrease in congenital malformations in newborn infants of an unselected population of diabetic women. Am J Obstet Gynecol 1989; 161:1163 – 1167.

70 Fuhrmann K, Reiher H, Semmler K, Glöckner E: The effect of intensified conventional insulin therapy before and during pregnancy on the malformation rate in offspring of diabetic mothers. Exp Clin Endocrinol 1984;83:173 – 177.

71 Goldman JA, Dicker D, Feldberg D, Yeshaya A, Samuel N, Karp M: Pregnancy outcome in patients with insulin-dependent diabetes mellitus with preconceptional diabetic control: A comparative study. Am J Obstet Gynecol 1986;155:293 – 297.

72 Tchobroutsky C, Bréart GL, Rambaud DC, Henrion R: Correlation between fetal defects and early growth delay observed by ultrasound. Lancet 1985;i:706 – 707.

73 Pedersen JF, Mølsted-Pedersen L: Early fetal growth delay detected by ultrasound marks increased risk of congenital malformation in diabetic pregnancy. Br Med J 1981;283:269 – 271.

74 Miodovnik M, Mimouni F, Tsang R, Ammar E, Kaplan L, Siddiqi TA: Glycemic control and spontaneous abortion in insulin-dependent diabetic women. Obstet Gynecol 1986;68:366 – 369.

75 Jongbloet PH: Abnormal infants and diabetic mothers. Lancet 1980;i:984 – 985.

76 Steel JM, Johnstone SD, Corrie JET: Early assessment of gestation in diabetics. Lancet 1984;ii: 975 – 976.

77 Naaktgeboren N, Devroey P, Wisanto A, Traey E, Van Steirteghem AC: Endocrine profiles in early pregnancies with delayed implantation. Hum Reprod 1986;1:9 – 14.

78 Ogata ES, Sabbagha R, Metzger BE, Phelps RL, Depp R, Freinkel N: Serial ultrasonography to assess evolving fetal macrosomia. JAMA 1980; 243:2405 – 2408.

79 Diamant YZ, Gale R: The fetus and the infant of

the diabetic mother; in Schenker JG, Weinstein D (eds): The Intrauterine Life – Management and Therapy. Amsterdam, Elsevier Science Publishers (Biomed Div), 1986, pp 23–30.
80 Keller JD, Metzger BE, Dooley SL, Tamura RK, Sabbagha RE, Freinkel N: Infants of diabetic mothers with accelerated fetal growth by ultrasonography: Are they all alike? Am J Obstet Gynecol 1990;163:893–897.
81 Visser GHA, van Ballegooie E, Sluiter WJ: Macrosomia despite well-controlled diabetic pregnancy. Lancet 1984;i:284–285.
82 Berk MA, Mimouni F, Miodovnik M, Hertzberg V, Valuck J: Macrosomia in infants of insulin-dependent diabetic mothers. Pediatrics 1989;83: 1029–1034.
83 Ballard JL, Holroyde J, Tsang RC, Chan G, Sutherland JM, Knowles HC: High malformation rates and decreased mortality in infants of diabetic mothers managed after the first trimester of pregnancy (1956–1978). Am J Obstet Gynecol 1984;148:1111–1118.
84 Fowden AL: The role of insulin in prenatal growth. J Dev Physiol 1989;12:173–182.
85 Strubbe JH: Central nervous system and insulin secretion. Neth J Med 1989;34:154–167.
86 Eriksson UJ: Congenital malformations in diabetic animal studies – A review. Diabetes Res 1984;1: 57–66.
87 Eriksson UJ, Lewis NJ, Freinkel N: Growth retardation during early organogenesis in embryos of experimentally diabetic rats. Diabetes 1984;33: 281–284.
88 Buchanan TA, Schemmer JK, Freinkel N: Embryotoxic effects of brief maternal insulin-induced hypoglycemia during organogenesis in the rat. J Clin Invest 1986;78:643–649.
89 Sadler TW, Hunter ES, Balkan W, Horton WE: Effects of maternal diabetes on embryogenesis. Am J Perinatol 1988;5:319–326.
90 Freinkel N: Diabetic embryopathy and fuel-mediated organ teratogenesis: Lessons from animal models. Horm Metab Res 1988;20:463–475.
91 Mulder EJH, Brader LJ, Verhoef A, Piersma AH, Visser GHA, Peters PWJ: Whole rat embryo culture in serum of insulin-dependent (type-1) diabetic women. Toxic In Vitro 1989;3:221–226.
92 Pinter E, Reece EA: Diabetes-associated congenital malformations: Epidemiology, pathogenesis, and experimental methods of induction and prevention; in Reece EA, Coustan DR (eds): Diabetes in Pregnancy. Principles and Practice. New York, Churchill Livingstone, 1988, pp 205–245.
93 Sadler TW, Hunter ES, Wynn RE, Phillips LS: Evidence for multifactorial origin of diabetes induced embryopathies. Diabetes 1989;38:70–74.
94 Reece EA, Scioscia AL, Pinter E, Hobbins JC, Green J, Mahoney MJ, Naftolin F: Prognostic significance of the human yolk sac assessed by ultrasonography. Am J Obstet Gynecol 1988;159: 1191–1194.
95 Zusman I, Yaffe P, Ornoy A: Effects of human diabetic serum on the in vitro development of mouse preimplantation embryos. Teratology 1989; 39:581–589.
96 De Hertogh R, Vanderheyden I, Pampfer S, Robin D, Dufrasne E, Delcourt J: Stimulatory and inhibitory effects of glucose and insulin on rat blastocyst development in vitro. Diabetes 1991; 40:641–647.

Dr. E.J.H. Mulder
University Hospital Utrecht
Department of Obstetrics and Gynaecology
Heidelberglaan 100
NL–3584 CX Utrecht (The Netherlands)

Dev Brain Dysfunct 1993;6:229–247

1019–5815/93/0065–0229$2.75/0

Intrauterine Effects of Coumarin Derivatives

Richard M. Pauli[a,b], *Joanne M. Haun*[b]

[a]Departments of Pediatrics and [b]Medical Genetics, University of Wisconsin-Madison, Madison, WI, USA

Key Words. Agenesis, corpus callosum · Anticoagulants · Central nervous system anomalies · Chondrodysplasia punctata · Coumarin derivatives · Dandy-Walker malformation · Optic atrophy · Pregnancy · Teratogenesis · Vitamin K · Warfarin embryiopathy

Abstract. The use of coumarin derivatives in pregnancy is associated with considerable risk for fetal sequelae. In particular, exposure in the first trimester may result in the warfarin embryopathy, while exposure, primarily in the second trimester, sometimes causes disruptional abnormalities of the central nervous system. We review here the progress which has been made over the past decade in understanding the embryopathologic mechanisms giving rise to these effects, in refining delineation of the specific clinical characteristics caused, and in estimating the level of fetal risk associated with intrauterine exposure.

Introduction

The coumarin derivatives are oral anticoagulants whose effects result from inhibition of function of vitamin-K-dependent factors within the coagulation cascade [1]. Their anticoagulation effect arises through specific inhibition of vitamin K epoxide reductase [2], an enzyme necessary for the interconversion of vitamin K and vitamin K epoxide [3]. In turn, vitamin K processing is required for it to function as a cofactor in the posttranslational modification of the precursors of coagulation factors II, VII, IX and X [4]. Postranslational γ-carboxylation of glutamyl residues in these proteins allows for calcium-dependent phospholipid binding by these proteins, which is essential for the normal enzymatic activity of these factors that is required for coagulation [4]. When coumarin derivatives, such as warfarin, are administered, they will thus cause inhibition of synthesis of the biologically active forms of these proteins, which are replaced by undercarboxylated, inactive forms and lead to consequent anticoagulant effects [5]. All coumarin derivatives function in this way; all appear to be associated with similar risks to the fetus. Therefore, they will be treated as a class in this review.

Risks of thrombotic and thromboembolic disease in pregnancy, in part conferred by the inherent hypercoagulable state of pregnant women, the increased survival of women with heart defects the treatment of which may require long-term anticoagulation, and the absence of any unequivocally equally effective alternative have, unfortunately, provided substantial opportunity to observe the effects of coumarin derivatives on the fetus. Coumarin derivative exposure of the fetus in fact can result in four distinct untoward effects, at least two of which have significant implications for the central nervous system: hemorrhagic effects in the newborn when used in the last stages of pregnancy, including risk for central nervous system hemorrhage; increased risk of spontaneous abortion; central nervous system disruptive effects and the warfarin embryopathy [6]. The last of these is the best understood and so will be reviewed first.

Recognition of the Warfarin Embryopathy

In 1966, DiSaia [7] described an infant who was the product of a pregnancy complicated by anticoagulant therapy in whom anomalies of ossification, nasal hypoplasia, small terminal phalanges and other birth defects were present. Just 2 years later, Kerber et al. [8] reported a similar constellation of abnormalities in 1 child exposed to oral anticoagulants *in utero*, as did Tejani [9] in 1973. As is often (and sometimes appropriately) the case, such single, retrospective case reports frequently remain buried in the literature without recognition that the commonalities described might reflect a serious teratogenic potential. The virtually simultaneous publication of 5 additional cases of specific birth defects associated with anticoagulant exposure, by Becker et al. [10], Shaul et al. [11] and Pettifor and Benson [12] in 1975, established warfarin and similar coumarin derivatives as potential human teratogens [13]. By 1980, 29 instances of what came to be known as the *warfarin embryopathy* had been recognized [6].

Features of the Warfarin Embryopathy

Hall et al. [6] published an extensive review which included details of these first 29 cases which materials will not be repeated here except in summary form. Subsequently, about two dozen additional cases with features of the warfarin embryopathy have been recognized and reported [14–32]. (Given that the phenotype was well established by 1980, certainly there are many more affected infants who have remained unreported). Table 1 summarizes the frequency of features demonstrated in 53 such cases. Virtually constant features of the warfarin embryopathy include nasal hypoplasia and, in those in whom appropriate radiologic investigations were completed, abnormalities of epiphyseal calcification. (Admittedly, establishing these as constant features has some element of tautology since it is likely that an individual would not be reported as having the warfarin embryopathy *without* these essential features.)

Typically, the nose is small, flattened and has unusual, perhaps unique, longitudinal septations between the nasal tip and the alae nasi (fig. 1). In many instances, the nasal septum is markedly hypoplastic, the nares small and, in some, the choanae are symptomatically stenotic. Hypoplasia of the nasal passages, in concert with the obligate nasal breathing of infants, frequently results in obstructive re-

Table 1. Summary of principal features reported in 53 instances of the warfarin embryopathy

Feature	Present/reported[1] n/n	Affected[2] %	Minimum Risk[2] %
Nasal hypoplasia	50/50	100	94
Periepiphyseal stippling	40/45	89	75
Limb hypoplasia (primarily distal digital hypoplasia)	18/36	50	34
Small for gestational age (< 10 percentile)	16/40	40	30
Respiratory distress/compromise as neonate	23/36	64	43
CNS abnormality	10/22	45	19
Ophthalmologic abnormality	6/36	17	11
Hearing loss/deafness	6/35	17	11
Congenital heart disease	2/30	7	4
Death	9/52	17	17

1 Reported reflects the number of instances in which published material or unpublished communication allows assignment in each of the feature categories as unaffected or affected.

2 Affected is simply the number affected over the number reported, while minimum risk assumes that all instances in which there were insufficient data about a feature can be assumed to have not had that feature. The real frequency of each of these characteristics in the warfarin embryopathy likely falls somewhere between the percentages given in these two columns.

spiratory distress, which can be relieved through use of an oral airway or through intubation [6].

The other principal marker of the warfarin embryopathy is a characteristic radiologic abnormality: punctate radiologic densities in normally uncalcified periepiphyseal regions. This 'stippling' is seen principally along the axial skeleton, at the proximal femora and in the calcanei (fig. 2) [6].

In addition to these virtually constant features, the other most common feature in babies with the warfarin embryopathy has been varying degrees of hypoplasia of the limbs. While occasional instances of marked rhizomelic shortening have been described, most often these are far more subtle distal digital changes [6].

With time, calcific stippling appears to become incorporated into ossifying epiphyses. Compensatory growth of the nose does not seem to occur, and facial features persist. Indeed, additional abnormalities of facial form may arise from dissynchronous and disproportionate growth [16].

Additional features, as summarized in table 1, may include, at a rather high frequency, central nervous system abnormalities. This does not mean that such central nervous system anomalies are an intrinsic part of the warfarin embryopathy, nor that the same mechanism of action as results in the embryopathy causes these central nervous system effects. Indeed, study of the 'genocopy' of the warfarin embryopathy and assessment of critical periods of effects both suggest that

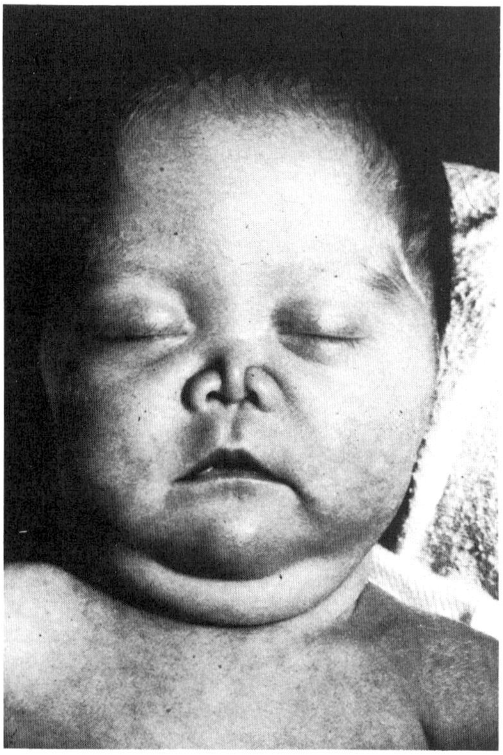

Fig. 1. Craniofacial features associated with the warfarin embryopathy. (Originally published in Pauli et al. [33], reproduced with permission from the publisher.)

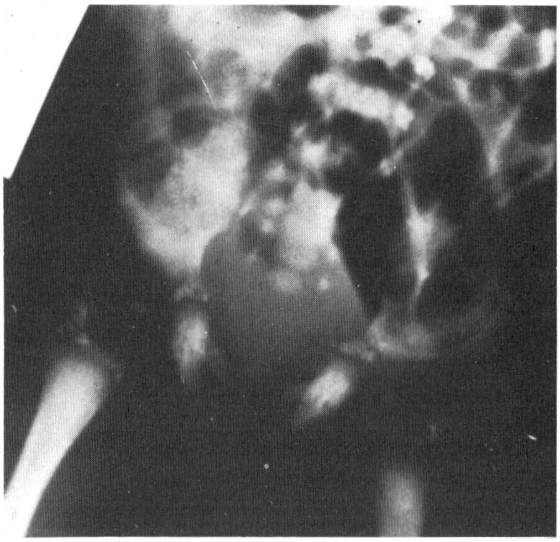

Fig. 2. Anteroposterior pelvis radiograph showing the stippling of periepiphyseal regions in an infant with the warfarin embryopathy. (Originally published in Pauli et al. [33], reproduced with permission from the publisher.)

separable, independent mechanisms give rise to the warfarin embryopathy per se and to the potentially far more devastating brain and eye-associated defects.

Critical Period of Effect in the Warfarin Embryopathy

The report of Pauli et al. [33] first established one limit of the period in embryogenesis during which exposure can result in the warfarin embryopathy through demonstration of typical features of this disorder in a baby from a pregnancy in which coumarin derivative exposure did not begin until the 6th gestational week. Analysis of exposure periods from all cases [6], those described by Holmes [pers. commun.], Johnson [pers. commun.], Lutz [pers. commun.] and Harrod [34] also being particularly crucial, strongly suggests that the window of exposure times which may give rise to the warfarin embryopathy is between the 6th and 9th week of gestation.

Table 2. Comparison of clinical features of the warfarin embryopathy and its genetic phenocopy, the so-called pseudowarfarin embryopathy which is secondary to a deficiency of vitamin K epoxide reductase activity

Feature	Warfarin embryopathy	Pseudowarfarin embryopathy
Nasal hypoplasia	+ + +	+ +
Stippled epiphyses	+ + +	+ to + +
Brachydactyly	+	+
Distal digital hypoplasia	+	+
Upper airway obstruction	+ to + +	+
CNS abnormality	+ / −	−
Warfarin exposure	+ + +	−
Persistent coagulopathy	−	+ +

+ / − = Subjective assessment of presence, frequency and severity of or absence of those features listed. Note concordance for the defining characteristics of the warfarin embryopathy.

Mechanism Giving Rise to the Warfarin Embryopathy

Since its initial description, most have assumed that the warfarin embryopathy arises from some primary pharmacologic action of the coumarin derivatives. Indeed, it was initially postulated that the features were a direct result of hemorrhage secondary to inhibition of fetal coagulation factors [10]. That, of course, was made extremely unlikely when the critical period of effect was shown to be around 6 – 9 weeks gestation, in concert with the recognized later development of vitamin-K-dependent coagulation proteins [35], which are undetectable until around 12 – 14 weeks gestation [36]. That suggested that either some other vitamin-K-dependent system must be central in these effects or that an action unrelated to the known pharmacologic action of coumarin derivatives is operative. The latter is not completely unreasonable; indeed, the lack of relationship between primary pharmacologic intent and teratogenic effects is likely one reason why precise mechanisms of teratogenicity of human teratogens have been so difficult to demonstrate [37]. Unfortunately, no appropriate animal model has been generated [38, 39]; ultimate demonstration of the effects giving rise to the embryopathy would have to depend on human experience.

It was our good fortune to be presented with an opportunity to indirectly demonstrate the mechanism giving rise to the embryopathic effects of coumarin derivatives. The stage for this recognition was set by basic investigations which demonstrated that there were, indeed, other vitamin-K-dependent, warfarin-inhibitable, but noncoagulation proteins [40 – 41]. Furthermore, at least two of these proteins, osteocalcin and matrix Gla protein, appear to have calcium binding or calcium deposition regulatory functions in bone and cartilage [42]. As detailed elsewhere [43], we investigated a single individual, unexposed to any anticoagulants in utero, who had both an inherent abnormality of function of all of the vitamin-K-dependent coagulation factors *and* all of the essential features of the warfarin embryopathy (table 2). (Subsequently, 3 other male children with this combination of characteristics have been recognized [44; unpubl.

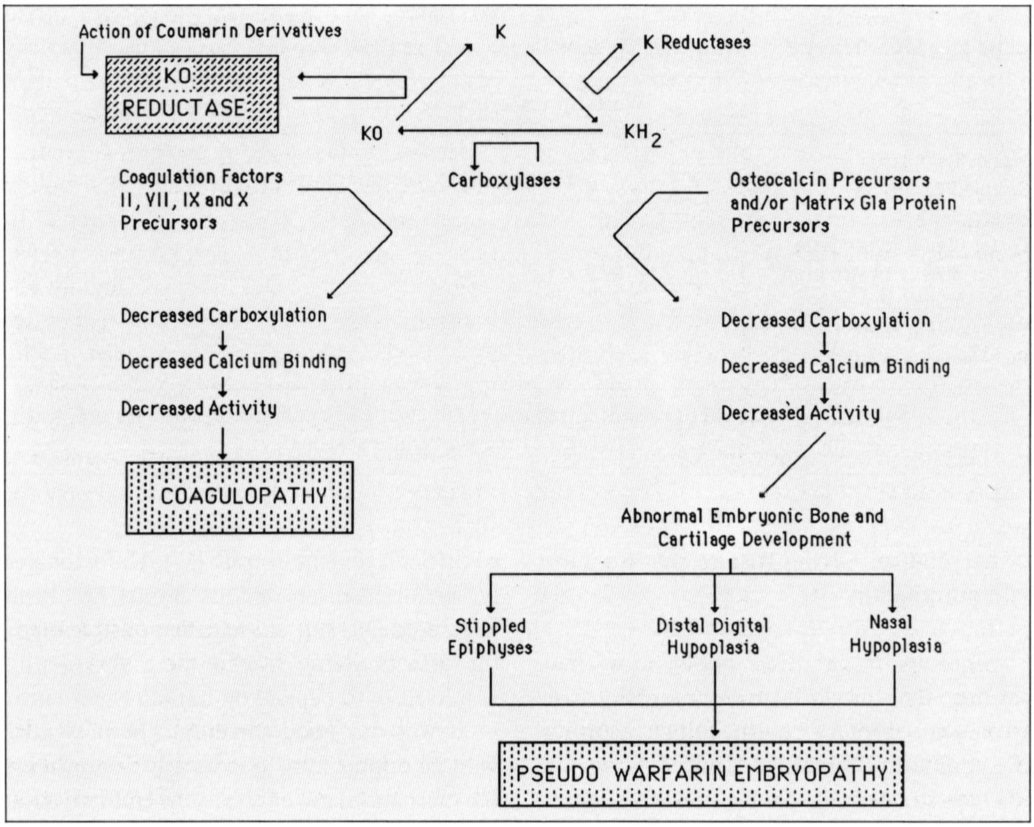

Fig. 3. Proposed biochemical mechanism giving rise to the combination of features present in children with the so-called pseudowarfarin embryopathy secondary to vitamin K epoxide reductase deficiency.

observations]). Biochemical investigations have confirmed generalized undercarboxylation of coagulation factors. This could either result from abnormalities of the protein carboxylases per se or, more interestingly, from abnormalities of the warfarin-inhibitable enzyme, vitamin K epoxide reductase [43]. Excesses of vitamin K epoxide in plasma in 2 of these children strongly suggest that their phenotypic features are a direct consequence of abnormalities of vitamin K epoxide reductase [45].

The most parsimonious explanation then is that the vitamin-K-dependent coagulopathy and the phenotypic features which are so similar to those of the warfarin embryopathy both arise from abnormal functioning of this enzyme. These individuals also have abnormalities of vitamin-K-dependent, calcium-binding bone protein. How then might these features explain the primary characteristics of the warfarin embryopathy? Both osteocalcin and matrix Gla protein are vitamin-K-dependent, γ-carboxyglutamyl residue containing, and warfarin inhibitable [42]. Both appear embryologically at a time consistent with the known critical period for exposure to coumarin derivatives to result in the embryopathy [41]. Both have been postulated to have some important function in control of calcium deposition in embryonic cartilage and bone [42]. All of the essential features of the warfarin embryopathy result from either abnormalities of calcium deposition or from abnormalities of cartilage growth. One might, therefore, postulate that these effects are secondary to the pharmacologic effects of warfarin on posttranslational carboxylation of one or both of these compounds. Then, *if* this were true and *if* there were some inborn error of metabolism which caused inhibition of all vitamin-K-dependent function, we would predict that it would result in both a vitamin K coagulopathy *and* a 'genocopy' of the warfarin embryopathy. That, indeed, is exactly what was found. At least by inference then the embryopathic effects of coumarin derivatives are almost certainly directly the result of the primary pharmacologic effect of warfarin, i.e. inhibition of vitamin K epoxide reductase (fig. 3) [43]. Currently, we are attempting to determine if there is a directly demonstrable vitamin K epoxide reductase deficiency in individuals with this disorder, which has come to be known as the pseudowarfarin embryopathy.

Individuals with the pseudowarfarin embryopathy do not uniformly have central nervous system effects. Those effects which are present seem to be the result of subsequent hemorrhagic complications [unpubl. observation]. This supports the notion that the embryopathic and central nervous system effects of warfarin on the embryo are separate and independent processes which overlap only because continual exposure of a particular fetus throughout gestation may place it at risk for multiple complications.

The warfarin embryopathy may serve as a model for understanding the pathogenetic processes underlying a group of human disorders which are characterized by stippling of epiphyses and periepiphyseal cartilage. In fact, there appear to be two primary mechanisms which may result in such stippling: abnormalities of vitamin K epoxide reductase, as in the pseudowarfarin embryopathy, the warfarin embryopathy, hydantoin exposure, etc. and peroxisomal abnormalities, as are demonstrable in the Zellweger syndrome, rhizomelic chondrodysplasia punctata and so forth (fig. 4) [45–48].

Central Nervous System Effects of *in utero* Exposure to Coumarin Derivatives

Nearly 50 years ago von Sydow [49] described a child with neonatal hydrocephalus who had been exposed throughout gestation to an oral anticoagulant. While it is impossible to assess in this particular case whether or not the hydrocephalus arose from perinatal hemorrhage, it has generally been assumed that central nervous system effects are of hemorrhagic origin. Perinatal hemorrhage is of serious concern in pregnancies requiring maternal anticoagulant therapy. Those risks have led to a generally accepted recommendation that oral anticoagulants be discontinued prior to the onset of labor [50].

However, there are a number of instances of central nervous system sequelae of intrauterine exposure to oral anticoagulants which cannot be so easily explained. Hall et al. [6] summarized 13 such cases. Subsequently, similar occurrences have accumulated. Tables 3 and 4 summarize 24 individuals in

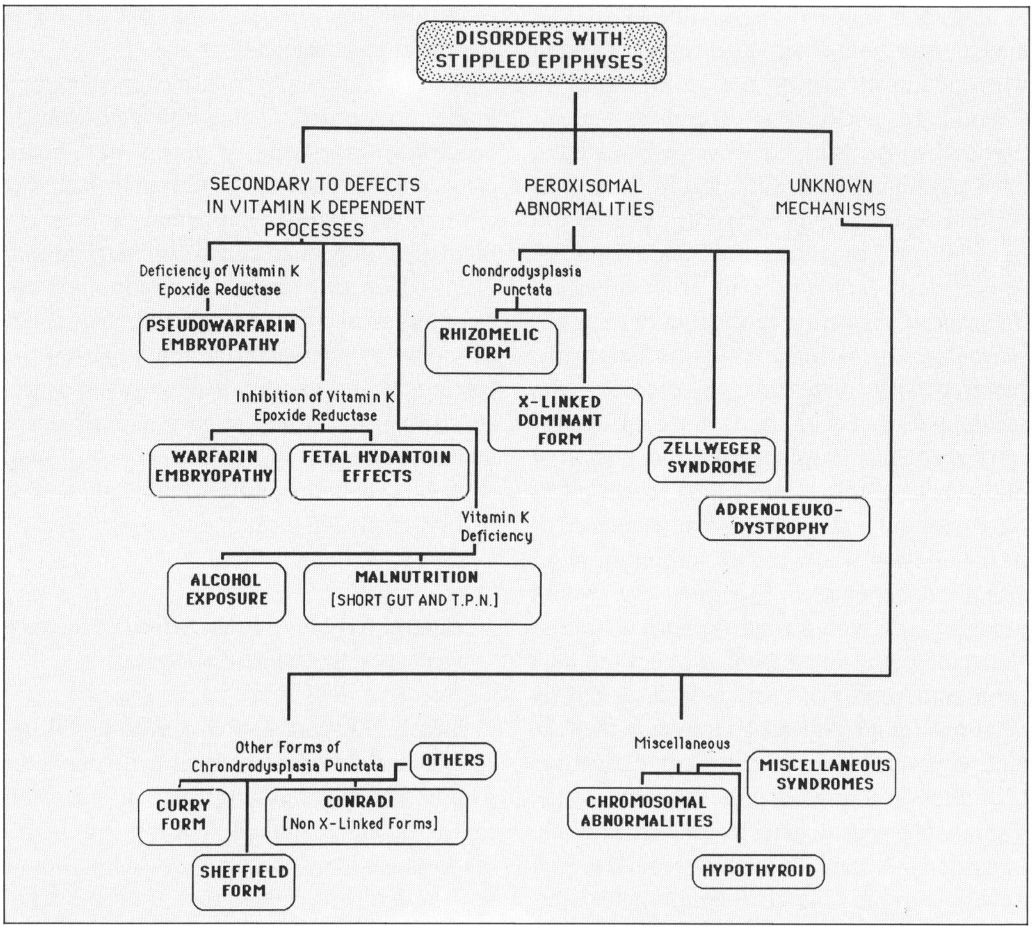

Fig. 4. Chart of disorders with stippled epiphyses organized by likely primary mechanism: those probably related to abnormalities of vitamin-K-dependent processes, those which are likely secondary to peroxisomal defects and those in which a mechanism cannot yet be postulated. T.P.N. = Total parenteral nutrition.

whom antenatal oral anticoagulant therapy has been associated with central nervous system abnormalities *not* straightforwardly explained by perinatal hemorrhage. In most the oral anticoagulant had been discontinued prior the onset of labor. (Furthermore, in only one instance was an incidental and unrelated event, sufficient in itself to explain the central nervous system dysfunction, present [58].)

Central Nervous System Effects as Distinct and Separate from the Warfarin Embryopathy

In less than half (9/23) of the 24 infants were features of the warfarin embryopathy present (table 3). That only a minority of infants with central nervous system effects show typical features of the warfarin embryopathy

Table 3. Non-central nervous system characteristics in 24 instances of central nervous system effects following exposure to coumarin derivatives

Author and reference	Anticoagulant	Weeks gestation of exposure	Presence or absense of features of the warfarin embryopathy
(1) Quenneville et al. [51]	Warfarin	24 – 40	Absent
(2) DiSaia [7]	Warfarin	0 – 26,28 – 36	Present
(3) Kerber et al. [8]	Warfarin	0 – 31	Present
(4) Tejani [9]	Warfarin	0 – 35	Present
(5) Hall [unpubl.]	Warfarin	16 – 24	Absent
(6) Pettifor and Benson [12]	Phenindione	0 – 41	Present
(7) Sherman and Hall [52]	Warfarin	14 – 38	Absent
(8) Pauli et al. [33]	Warfarin	6 – 32	Present
(9) Warkany and Bofinger [53]	Warfarin	6 – 16	Absent
(10) Warkany and Bofinger [53]	Warfarin	0 – 35	Absent
(11) Carson and Reid [54]	Warfarin	10 – 36	Absent
(12) Holzgreve et al. [55]	Warfarin	0 – 15	Absent
(13) Pauli [unpubl.]	Warfarin	6 – 40	Absent
(14) Guillot et al. [56]	Acenocoumarin	0 – 28	Present
(15) Stevenson et al. [57]	Warfarin	0 – 31	Present
(16) Whitfield [58]	Warfarin	0 – 20	Present
(17) Larrea et al. [21]	Acenocoumarin	'1st & 2nd trimester'	Present
(18) Chen et al. [59]	Warfarin	0 – 36	Absent
(19) Kort and Cassel [60]	Warfarin	Uncertain	Absent
(20) LaPiedra et al. [61]	Acenocoumarin	0 – 6 + uncertain	Unknown
(21) Kaplan et al. [62]	Warfarin	0 – 16,17 – 33	Absent
(22) Kaplan [63]	Warfarin	8 – 12	Absent
(23) Sheikhzadeh et al. [64]	Warfarin	0 – 32	Absent
(24) Pauli [unpubl.]	Warfarin	14 – 20	Absent

and, conversely, that a minority of those with the warfarin embryopathy have central nervous system involvement (table 1) strongly suggests that independent teratogenic mechanisms are likely to be operative.

Similarly, timing of exposures suggests that an independent process gives rise to the central nervous system effects following intrauterine coumarin derivative exposure. Note that cases 1, 5, 7, 11 and 24 in table 3 were not exposed during the weeks 6 – 9 of pregnancy (the critical period of exposure for development of the warfarin embryopathy). Indeed, there seems to be *no* time in gestation during which all infants with central nervous system effects were exposed. If there is a critical window of exposure, and assuming that all affected infants suffered damage through a similar mechanism, then this window must extend from at least 12 weeks (the latest point of exposure in ref. [63]) through 24 weeks gestation (the earliest period of exposure in ref. [51]).

A recently described animal model also

Table 4. Central nervous system, cognitive and ophthalmologic characteristics in 24 instances of central nervous system effects following exposure to coumarin derivative

Author and reference	Primary Structural CNS characteristics	Functional CNS characteristics	Severity of effects	Ophthalmologic characteristics
(1) Quenneville et al. [51]	Microcephaly; Cerebral agenesis	–	Disabling	Optic atrophy
(2) DiSaia [7]	–	Mild MR; blind	Disabling	Optic atrophy
(3) Kerber et al. [8]	–	Moderate-severe MR; seizures; deaf; spasticity	Disabling	–
(4) Tejani [9]	Occipital meningocele; hydrocephalus	Severe MR	Disabling	Microphthalmia
(5) Hall [unpubl.]	Cerebellar atrophy; cerebral atrophy	Moderate MR; seizures; spasticity	Disabling	Optic atrophy
(6) Pettifor and Benson [12]	–	Mild MR	Disabling	Optic atrophy
(7) Sherman and Hall [52]	Microcephaly	MR; hypotonia	Disabling	?Blind
(8) Pauli et al. [33]	Cerebral atrophy	MR; hypotonia	Lethal	–
(9) Warkany and Bofinger [53]	Hydrocephalus	–	Lethal	–
(10) Warkany and Bofinger [53]	DWM; parieto-occipital encephalocele; hydrocepahlus	–	Disabling	–
(11) Carson and Reid [54]	Microcephaly	MR; spasticity	Disabling	Blind
(12) Holzgreve et al. [55]	Posterior fossa cyst (?DWM); possible ACC	Mild-moderate MR;	Disabling	–

DWM = Dandy Walker malformation; ACC = agenesis of the corpus callosum; MR = mental retardation.

supports the idea of an independent, late gestational origin of central nervous system effects of coumarin derivatives. Howe and Webster [65] exposed pregnant rats to warfarin and vitamin K. With mid- and late gestational exposures, hemorrhagic changes were induced, with principal effects including damage to the brain and to the eye.

It seems most likely that the deleterious effects of coumarin derivatives arise through multiple critical periods (and multiple mechanisms) during gestation. Certainly, they can cause primary hemorrhagic complications when exposure occurs near delivery. Nearly as certainly, the warfarin embryopathy results from exposure between the 6th and 9th gestational weeks. Most likely, most of the central nervous system effects being considered here arise because of second trimester exposure.

Author and reference	Primary Structural CNS characteristics	Functional CNS characteristics	Severity of effects	Ophthalmologic characteristics
(13) Pauli [unpubl.]	DWM; possible ACC	Mild MR; spasticity	Disabling	–
(14) Guillot et al. [56]	Microcephaly	Delayed; hypotonia	Disabling	–
(15) Stevenson et al. [57]	–	Delayed	Disabling	Optic atrophy
(16) Whitfield [58]	–	Delayed; hemiparesis; meningoencephalitis at 9 months	Incidental	–
(17) Larrea et al. [21]	–	Moderate MR	Disabling	–
(18) Chen et al. [59]	Hydrocephalus	MR	Disabling	–
(19) Kort and Cassel [60]	Meningomyelocele	–	Unknown	–
(20) LaPiedra et al. [61]	Hydrocephalus	–	Unknown	–
(21) Kaplan et al. [62]	DWM; hydrocephalus; absent septum pellucidum	–	Disabling	–
(22) Kaplan [63]	DWM; ACC; hydrocephalus	Mild MR; seizures	Disabling	Peter anomaly
(23) Sheikhzadeh et al. [64]	Anencephaly	–	Lethal	–
(24) Pauli [unpubl.]	Cerebral atrophy; microcephaly; posterior fossa cyst	Moderate MR; seizures; spasticity	Disabling	–

Patterns of Abnormalities and Mechanism of Production of Central Nervous System Anomalies

Are the central nervous system effects of *in utero* coumarin derivative exposure utterly nonspecific or can particular patterns of effects be discerned? Of the 24 cases summarized in table 4, at least 8 (33%) had features suggestive of septo-optic dysplasia or similar anomalies, including optic atrophy in 5 (as well as microphthalmia in 1 and unexplained blindness in 2 others), agenesis of the corpus callosum in 3 and absence of the septum pellucidum in 1. In addition, 6 (25%) had a Dandy-Walker malformation or similar posterior fossa abnormality (fig. 5). Finally, there was 1 encephalocele, 1 meningocele, 1 meningomyelocele and 1 instance of anencephaly. Three distinct patterns of effect, therefore,

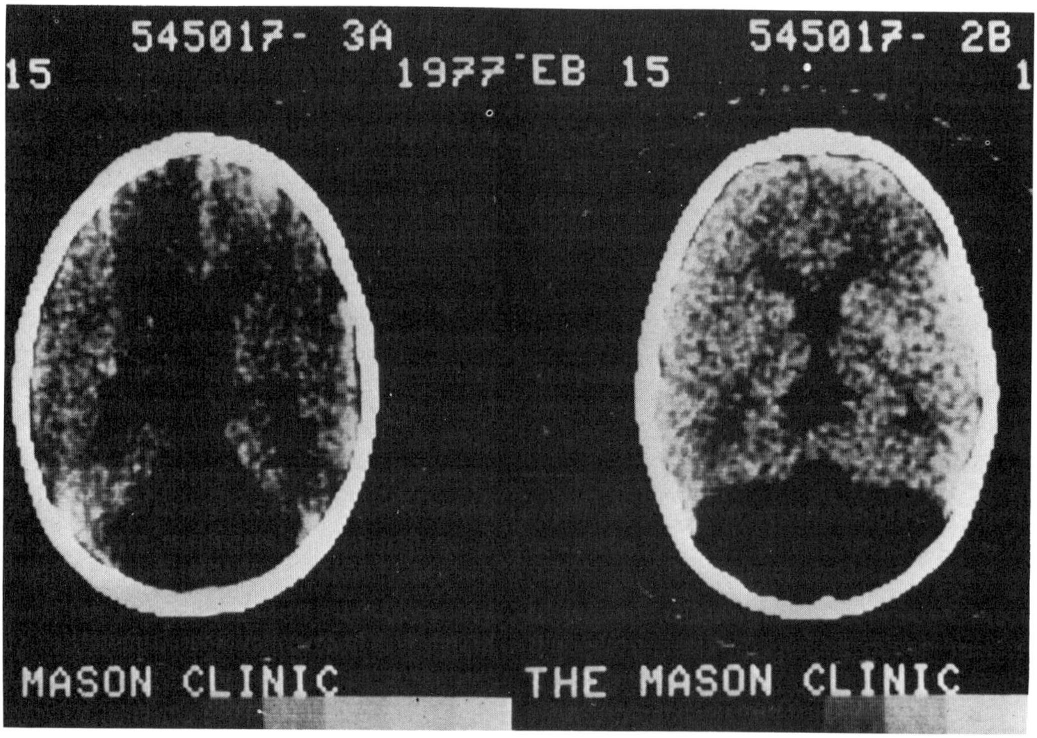

Fig. 5. Computerized tomographic scan of an early instance of central nervous system abnormalities associated with coumarin derivative exposure, showing a prominent posterior fossa cyst.

seem to emerge: septo-optic dysplasia, Dandy-Walker malformation, and neural tube defects. That these are the particular, recurrent patterns seen lends further support to the idea that the origin of the central nervous system abnormalities are vascular based disruptive events. There have been suggestions that each of these three patterns of anomalies – Dandy-Walker malformation [66], septo-optic dysplasia [67] and neural tube defects [68] – may at least sometimes arise not from intrinsic abnormalities of the involved structures per se, but because of secondary disruption caused by vascular or hemorrhagic accidents. (Admittedly, this portion of the argument remains weak. Note, for example, that each of these three abnormalities are relatively frequently associated with each other in the same individuals in circumstances in which anticoagulant exposure has not occurred and in circumstances in which hemorrhage or vascular abnormalities seem unlikely to have occurred. [66, 69])

There are multiple indirect lines of evidence supporting the idea that central nervous system effects of intrauterine coumarin derivative exposure arise from secondary disruptions. Certainly, one might posit that these disruptive effects are a direct consequence of coumarin derivative effects on coagulation factors in the developing fetus. There is only a single example which remains problematic in this regard. Kaplan [63] described an infant with Dandy-Walker malformation, agenesis of the corpus callosum, as well as Peter anomaly of the eye. Exposure apparently occurred only between the 8th and 12th weeks of gestation. While there is no independent documentation (e.g. ultrasonography) of the accuracy of this dating, this single case at least suggests that central nervous system anomalies might result from first trimester exposure (prior to the development of coagulation factors in the fetus) and might, at least in some instances, be malformational rather than disruptional.

Other Malformations Reported in Association with Coumarin Derivative Exposure

Various other birth defects have been recognized following exposure to coumarin derivatives in utero. These include, for example, at least 4 instances of congenital heart disease [6, 70, 71], 3 of cleft lip and palate [59, 60, 72], 3 with renal and genitourinary anomalies [53, 72, 73], 1 with congenital hip dysplasia [60], 1 with diaphragmatic hernia [74] and so forth [59, 72, 75]. Either coumarin derivative exposure nonspecifically increases risks for common birth defects, or certain of these abnormalities may have arisen through yet other teratogenic mechanisms, or these associations may be coincidental and of no significance. The last seems most likely.

Estimations of Risk

As part of their review published in 1980, Hall et al. [6] attempted to estimate risks of adverse effects of intrauterine coumarin derivative exposure. Of necessity, those estimates were based upon review of all published instances of exposure. Obviously, such methods introduce ascertainment biases of unknown effect, but which most likely would overestimate the risks. Their estimate of risk for embryopathic manifestations was about 4% (16/418), while risk of central nervous system effects (not including sequelae of perinatal hemorrhage) was estimated to be about 3% (11/418).

Ginsberg and Hirsh [76–78] and Ginsberg et al. [79] have subsequently attempted to refine estimates of risk of adverse outcome following various forms of anticoagulation in pregnancy. Their series of four articles [76–79], all based upon the same literature-derived data set, does significantly improve upon previous assessments of the risks of heparin. In arriving at risk estimates for embryopathic and central nervous system effects of coumarin derivatives, the same publication based ascertainment bias found in Hall et al. [6] is to be anticipated. Nevertheless, Ginsberg and Hirsh [76–78] and Ginsberg et al. [79] do provide an additional, updated rough estimate of risks. Within 970 published gestational exposures to coumarin derivatives, they found 45 instances of the warfarin embryopathy and 16 of central nervous system effects, which we would judge not to be related to perinatal hemorrhage, yielding risk estimates of about 4.7 and 1.6%, respectively.

Some of the biases obvious in such review may be eliminated by using only published *series* of coumarin derivative treatment in pregnancy. Additional bias might be minimized by using only relatively recent studies (given the changes in overall medical care which occur over time). We have found 15 such studies which have been published since 1980 [17, 18, 21, 24–26, 58, 59, 63, 80–85]. These vary

Table 5. Summary of outcomes in published series of warfarin exposure in pregnancy: study design

Study	Type of study[1]	Anticoagulant	Weeks used	n
Ben Ismail et al. [80]	Retrospective Sequential Single institution Prosthetic valves	'Oral'	Not stated	53
Braun et al. [81]	Retrospective Sequential Single institution Prosthetic valves	Acenocoumarin	'Throughout'	24
Chen et al. [59]	Retrospective Sequential – Prosthetic valves	Warfarin	Variable	30
Chong et al. [82]	Retrospective follow-up 46 pregancies 22 of 42 eligible examined Two institutions Various	Warfarin	Variable	46
Iturbe-Alessio et al. [17]	Prospective Sequential: 35 of 49 infants examined Multiple institutions Prosthetic valves	Acenocoumarin	Variable	49
Javares et al. [18]	Retrospective Sequential Single institution Prosthetic valves	Acenocoumarin	0 to 34–36 weeks	29
Kort and Cassel [60]	Retrospective Sequential Single institution Cardiac disease	Warfarin	Variable	40
Larrea et al. [21]	Retrospective Sequential Single institution Prosthetic valves	Acenocoumarin	Variable	47

[1] Showing whether the study was retrospective or prospective, whether patients included were generally sequential or selected, whether one or more than one institutional setting was included and the indications for

in design and size (table 5). Most are retrospective. Few (e.g. [17, 25, 82]) had careful infant examination or follow-up, and even in those which did, the proportion of eligible infants examined was often quite small. Despite these limitations, these studies can provide another estimate of risks (table 6). In generating this table, instances of embryopathy were judged to be either 'certain' (when reasonably complete description of typically affected children is provided) or 'possible' (including the first group, but, in

Study	Type of study[1]	Anticoagulant	Weeks used	n
Lee et al. [83]	Retrospective Sequential Single institution Prosthetic valves	Warfarin	0 to 6–8 and 13 to 37 weeks	18
Matorras et al. [84]	Retrospective Sequential Single institution Prosthetic valves	Warfarin	0 to 37–38 weeks	44
O'Neill et al. [24]	Retrospective Sequential Four institutions Prosthetic valves	Warfarin	Variable	17
Parankumar et al. [85]	Retrospective Sequential Single institution Prosthetic valves	Acenocoumarin	'Throughout'	47
Salazar et al. [25]	Retrospective Sequential: 34 of 128 infants examined Single institution Prosthetic valves	Acenocoumarin	0 to 38 weeks	128
Sarelli et al. [26]	Prospective Sequential Single institution Prosthetic valves	Warfarin	1st & 2nd trimester	50
Sheikhzadeh et al. [64]	Retrospective Sequential Single institution Prosthetic valves	Warfarin	0 to 39 weeks	13
Total				635

anticoagulation in the patients assessed.

addition, those ill-described and/or apparently subtly affected). Among 635 pregnancies and 485 liveborns in these studies, only 8 certainly had features of the warfarin embryopathy (1.3% of pregnancies and 1.6% of liveborns), while broad inclusion criteria yield 20 possibly affected infants (3.1% of pregnancies and 4.1% of liveborns). Central nervous system effects are even less frequent (recognizing, of course, that these even more than the embryopathic effects might be underascertained without careful follow-up): only 4 infants

Table 6. Summary of outcomes in published series of warfarin exposure in pregnancy: fetal outcome[1]

Study	Total	Abortion		Stillbirth		Neonatal death		Embryopathy, n		CNS/ ophthalmologic, n
		n	%	n	%	n	%	certain	possible	
Ben Ismail et al. [80]	53	8	15	3	6	4	8	0	0	0
Braun et al. [81]	24	7	29	5	21			0	0	0
Chen et al. [59]	30	10	33	0		0		0	0	1
Chong et al. [82]	46	?		2	4	2	4	0	0	0
Iturbe-Alessio et al. [17]	49	9	18	1	2	0		2	8	0
Javares et al. [18]	29	?		?		?		0	1	0
Kort and Cassel [60]	40	2	5	3	7	0		0	0	1
Larrea et al. [21]	47	11	23	0		1	2	2	2	1
Lee et al. [83]	18	9	50	0		0		0	0	0
Matorras et al. [84]	44	8	18	0		1	2	1	2	0
O'Neill et al. [24]	17	6	35	2	12	0		1	1	0
Parankumar et al. [85]	47	3	6	1	2	1	2	0	0	0
Salazar et al. [25]	128	36	28	9	7	3	2	1	3	0
Sarelli et al. [26]	50	9	18	7	14	2	4	1	2	0
Sheikhzadeh et al. [64]	13	2	15	2	15	2	15	0	1	1
Total	635	120	20	30	5	16	3	8	20	4

The total percentages for certain and possible embryopathies were 1.3 and 3.1%, respectively. Total CNS/ophthalmologic = 0.6%.

[1] Because of differences in the manner that adverse outcomes are tabulated in various studies, the data from one to another are not strictly comparable and the totals should be viewed with this in mind.

had central nervous system and/or ophthalmologic abnormalities (0.6% of pregnancies and 0.8% of liveborns).

Given the limitations of all of these estimates, nonetheless we think that reasonable ranges of risk, which can be used in a clinical setting, can be made. The warfarin embryopathy will occur in about *1.5–5%* of exposed infants and only if exposure occurs between 6 and 9 weeks gestation. Risks for central nervous system effects are even less, probably in the range of *0.5–2%* and most often resulting from second trimester exposure.

References

1 Suttle JW: Current concepts of the mechanism of action of vitamin K and its antagonists: in Lindenbaum J (ed): Nutrition in Hematology. New York, Churchill Linvingstone, 1983, pp 245–270.
2 Gallop PM, Lian JB, Hauschka PV: Carboxylated calcium-binding proteins and vitamin K. N Engl J Med 1980;302:1460–1466.
3 Suttle JW: Carboxylation of glutamyl residues; in Freedman RB, Hawkins HC (eds): The Enzymology of Post-Translational Modification of Proteins. London, Academic Press, 1980, pp 213–258.
4 Davie EW, Fujikawa K: Basic mechanisms of blood coagulation. Annu Rev Biochem 1975;44:799–829.

5 Fasco MJ, Hildebrandt EF, Suttle JW: Evidence that warfarin anticoagulant action involves two distinct reductase activities. J Biol Chem 1982;257: 11210 – 11212.
6 Hall JG, Pauli RM, Wilson KM: Maternal and fetal sequelae of anticoagulation during pregnancy. Am J Med 1980;68:122 – 140.
7 DiSaia PJ: Pregnancy and delivery of a patient with a Starr-Edwards mitral valve prosthesis. Report of a case. Obstet Gynecol 1966;28: 469 – 472.
8 Kerber IJ, Warr OS, Richardson C: Pregnancy in a patient with a prosthetic mitral valve. JAMA 1968;203:223 – 225.
9 Tejani N: Anticoagulant therapy with cardiac valve prosthesis during pregnancy. Obstet Gynecol 1973; 42:785 – 793.
10 Becker MH, Genieser MB, Finegold M, Miranda D, Spackman T: Chondrodysplasia punctata. Is maternal warfarin therapy a factor? Am J Dis Child 1975:129:356 – 359.
11 Shaul WL, Emery H, Hall JG: Chondrodysplasia punctata and maternal warfarin use during pregnancy. Am J Dis Child 1975;129:360 – 362.
12 Pettifor JM, Benson R: Congenital malformations associated with the administration of oral anticoagulants during pregnancy. J Pediatr 1975;88: 459 – 462.
13 Warkany J: A warfarin embryopathy? Am J Dis Child 1975;129:287 – 288.
14 Baillie M, Allen ED, Elkington AR: The congenital warfarin syndrome: A case report. Br J Ophthalmol 1980;64:633 – 635.
15 Curtin T, Mulhern B: Foetal warfarin syndrome. Ir Med J 1980;73:393 – 394.
16 Hosenfeld D, Wiedemann HR: Chondrodysplasia punctata in an adult recognized as vitamin K antagonist embryopathy. Clin Genet 1989;35:376 – 381.
17 Iturbe-Alessio I, Fonseca M, Mutchinik O, Santos MA, Zajarias A, Salazar E: Risks of anticoagulant therapy in pregnant women with artificial heart valves. N Engl J Med 1986;315: 1390 – 1393.
18 Javares T, Coto EO, Maiques V, Rincon A, Such M, Caffarena JM: Pregnancy after heart valve replacement. Int J Cardiol 1984;5:731 – 739.
19 Jullian M, Youlton R, Rivera L: Embriopatia por anticoagulante oral. Rev Méd Chile 1983;111: 1045 – 1048.
20 Lamontagne JM, Leclerc JE, Carrier C, Bureau M: Warfarin embryopathy – A case report. J Otolaryngol 1984;13:127 – 129.
21 Larrea JL, Núñez L, Reque JA, GilAquado M, Matarros R, Minguez JA: Pregnancy and mechanical valve prostheses: A high-risk situation for the mother and the fetus. Ann Thorac Surg 1983;36:459 – 463.
22 Lanfranchi C, Olivier C, Boudot de la Motte E, Bavoux F: Anticoagulants et grossesse. Thérapie 1982;37:493 – 495.
23 Matorras R, Reque JA, Usandizaga JA, Minguez JA, Larrea JL, Núñez L: Prosthetic heart valve and pregnancy. A study of 59 cases. Gynecol Obstet Invest 1985;19:21 – 31.
24 O'Neill H, Blake S, Sugrue D, MacDonald D: Problems in the management of patients with artificial valves during pregnancy. Br J Obstet Gynaecol 1982;89:940 – 943.
25 Salazar E, Zajarias A, Gutierrez N, Iturbe I: The problem of cardiac valve prostheses, anticoagulants, and pregnancy. Circulation 1984; 70(suppl 1):169 – 177.
26 Sareli P, England MJ, Berk MR, Marcus RH, Epstein M, Driscoll J, Meyer T, McIntyre J, van Gelderen C: Maternal and fetal sequelae of anticoagulation during pregnancy in patients with mechanical heart valve prostheses. Am J Cardiol 1989;63:1462 – 1465.
27 Strüwe E, Reinwein H, Stier R: Coumarin-Embryopathie. Radiologe 1984;24:68 – 71.
28 Tamburrinni O, Bartolomeo-Deluri A, Di Guglielmo GL: Chondrodysplasia punctata after warfarin. Case report with 18-month follow-up. Pediatr Radiol 1987;17:323 – 324.
29 Weeninck GH, van Dijk-Wierda CA, Meyboom RHB, Koppe JG, Staalman CR, Treffers PE: Teratogeen effect van coumarine-derivaten. Ned Tijdschr Geneeskd 1981;125:702 – 706.
30 Whitfield MF: Chondrodysplasia punctata after warfarin in early pregnancy. Arch Dis Child 1980; 55:139 – 142.
31 Zakzouk MS: The congenital warfarin syndrome. J Laryngol Otol 1986;100:215 – 219.
32 Zipprich KW, Canzler E, Hundsdörfer S: Zur teratogenen Wirkung von Kumarinen. Zentralbl Gynäkol 1987;109:364 – 368.
33 Pauli RM, Madden JD, Kranzler KJ, Culpepper W, Port R: Warfarin therapy initiated during pregnancy and phenotypic chondrodysplasia punctata. J Pediatr 1976;88:506 – 508.

34 Harrod JE, Sherrod PS: Warfarin embryopathy in siblings. Obstet Gynecol 1981;57:673–676.
35 Forestier F, Daffos F, Rainaut M, Solé Y, Amiral J: Vitamin K dependent proteins in fetal hemostasis at mid trimester of pregnancy. Thromb Haemost 1985;53:401–403.
36 Bleyer WA, Hakami N, Shepard TH: The development of hemostasis in the human fetus and newborn infant. J Pediatr 1971;790:838–853.
37 Juchau MR (ed): The Biochemical Basis of Chemical Teratogenesis. New York, Elsevier, 1981.
38 Kronick J, Phelps NE, McCallion DJ, Hirsh J: Effects of sodium warfarin administered during pregnancy in mice. Am J Obstet Gynecol 1974; 118:819–823.
39 Feteih R, Tassinari MS, Lian JB: Effect of sodium warfarin on vitamin K-dependent proteins and skeletal development in the rat fetus. J Bone Miner Res 1990;5:885–894.
40 Hauschka PV, Lian JB, Gallop PM: Vitamin K and mineralization. Trends Biochem Sci 1978;3: 75–78.
41 Hauschka PV, Reid ML: Timed appearance of a calcium-binding protein containing gamma-carboxyglutamic acid in developing chick bone. Dev Biol 1978;65:426–434.
42 Hauschka PV, Lian JB, Cole DE, Gundberg CM: Osteocalcin and matrix Gla protein: Vitamin K-dependent proteins in bone. Physiol Rev 1989; 69:990–1047.
43 Pauli RM, Lian JB, Mosher DF, Suttie JW: Association of congenital deficiency of multiple vitamin K-dependent coagulation factors and the phenotype of the warfarin embryopathy: Clues to the mechanism of teratogenicity of coumarin derivatives. Am J Hum Genet 1987;41:566–583.
44 Leonard CO: Vitamin K responsive bleeding disorder: A genocopy of the warfarin embryopathy. Proc Greenwood Genet Cent 1988;7: 165–166.
45 Pauli RM: Mechanism of bone and cartilage maldevelopment in the warfarin embryopathy. Pathol Immunopathol Res 1988;7:107–112.
46 Sheffield LJ, Halliday JL, Jensen FO, Danks DM: To lump or split types of chondrodysplasia punctata? Proc Greenwood Genet Cent 1990;10: 112–113.
47 Toriello HV, Lin A, Higgins JV: Conditions with stippled epiphyses: Two new syndromes/situations and a review of the literature. Proc Greenwood Genet Cent 1990;10:113–114.
48 Badois C, Lavollay B, Bomsel F: Maladie des épiphyses ponctuées (MEP) associéè a une foetopathie éthyligue (FE). Trois premiers cas rapportés. Ann Radiol (Paris) 1983;26:244–250.
49 von Sydow G: Hypoprotrombinemi och hjärnskada hos barn till dikumarin-behandlad moder. Nord Med 1947;34:1171–1172.
50 Hirsh J, Cade JF, Gallus AS: Anticoagulants in pregnancy: A review of indications and complications. Am Heart J 1972;83:301–305.
51 Quenneville G, Barton B, McDevitt E, Wright I: The use of anticoagulants for thrombophlebitis during pregnancy. Am J Obstet Gynecol 1959;77: 1135–1149.
52 Sherman S, Hall BD: Warfarin and fetal abnormality. Lancet 1976;i:692.
53 Warkany J, Bofinger M: Le role de la coumadine dans les malformations congénitales. Med Hyg 1975;33:1454–1457.
54 Carson M, Reid M: Warfarin and fetal abnormality. Lancet 1976;i:1127.
55 Holzgreve W, Carey JC, Hall BD: Warfarin-induced fetal abnormalities. Lancet 1976;ii: 914–915.
56 Guillot M, Toubas PL, Mselati JC, Gamarra E, Moriette G, Relier JP: Embryo-foetopathie coumarinique et maladie des epiphyses ponctuées. Arch Fr Pédiatr 1979;36:63–66.
57 Stevenson RE, Burton OM, Ferlauto GJ, Taylor HA: Hazards of oral anticoagulants during pregnancy. JAMA 1980;243:1549–1551.
58 Whitfield MF: Chondrodysplasia punctata after warfarin in early pregnancy. Case report and summary of the literature. Arch Dis Child 1980;55: 139–142.
59 Chen WWC, Chan CS, Lee PK, Wang RY, Wong VCW: Pregnancy in patients with prosthetic heart valves: An experience with 45 pregnancies. Q J Med 1982;203:358–365.
60 Kort HI, Cassel GA: An appraisal of warfarin therapy during pregnancy. S Afr Med J 1981;60: 578–579.
61 LaPiedra OJ, Bernal JM, Ninot S, Gonzalez I, Pastor E, Miralles PJ: Open heart surgery for thrombosis of a prosthetic mitral valve during pregnancy. Fetal hydrocephalus. J Cardiovasc Surg 1986;27:217–220.
62 Kaplan LC, Anderson GG, Ring BA: Congenital

hydrocephalus and Dandy-Walker malformation associated with warfarin use during pregnancy. Birth Defects 1982;18[3A]:79 – 83.
63 Kaplan LC: Congenital Dandy Walker malformation associated with first trimester warfarin: A case report and literature review. Teratology 1985;32: 333 – 337.
64 Sheikhzadeh A, Ghabusi P, Kakim Sh, Wendler G, Sarram M: Congestive heart failure in valvular heart disease in pregnancies with and without valvular prostheses and anticoagulant therapy. Clin Cardiol 1983;6:465 – 470.
65 Howe AM, Webster WS: Exposure of the pregnant rat to warfarin and vitamin K1: An animal model of intraventricular hemorrhage in the fetus. Teratology 1990;42:413 – 420.
66 Pascual-Castroviejo I, Velez A, Pascual-Pascual SI, Roche MC, Villarejo F: Dandy-Walker malformation: Analysis of 38 cases. Childs Nerv Syst 1991;7:88 – 97.
67 Stevenson RE, Kelly JC, Aylsworth AS, Phelan MC: Vascular basis for neural tube defects: A hypothesis. Pediatrics 1987;80:102 – 106.
68 Lubinsky M: Vascular disruptive origin of septo-optic dysplasia. Greater Wisconsin Genetics Exchange 1991.
69 Murray JC, Johnson JA, Bird TD: Dandy Walker malformation: Etiologic heterogeneity and empiric recurrence risks. Clin Genet 1985;28:272 – 283.
70 Balde MD, Breitbach GP, Wettstein A, Hoffmann W, Bastert G: Fallotsche Tetralogie nach Cumarineinnahme in Frühschwangerschaft – Eine Embryopathie? Geburtshilfe Frauenheilkd 1988;48: 182 – 183.
71 Dean H, Berliner S, Shoenfeld Y, Pinkhas J: Warfarin treatment during pregnancy in patients with prosthetic mitral valves. Acta Haematol (Basel) 1981;66:65 – 66.
72 Ayhan A, Yapar EG, Yüce K, Kisnisci HA, Nazli N, Özmen F: Pregnancy and its complications after cardiac valve replacement. Int J Gynaecol Obstet 1991;35:117 – 122.
73 Hall BD: Warfarin embryopathy and urinary tract anomalies: Possible new association. Am J Med Genet 1989;34:292 – 293.
74 Normann EK, Stray-Pedersen B: Warfarin-induced fetal diaphragmatic hernia. Case report. Br J Obstet Gynaecol 1989;96:729 – 730.
75 Ruthnum P, Tolmie JL: Atypical malformations in an infant exposed to warfarin during the first trimester of pregnancy. Teratology 1987;36: 299 – 301.
76 Ginsberg JS, Hirsh J: Optimum use of anticoagulants in pregnancy. Drugs 1988;36: 505 – 512.
77 Ginsberg JS, Hirsh J: Anticoagulants during pregnancy. Annu Rev Med 1989;40:79 – 86.
78 Ginsberg JS, Hirsh J: Use of anticoagulants during pregnancy. Chest 1989;95(suppl):156 – 160.
79 Ginsberg JS, Hirsh J, Turner DC, Levine MN, Burrows R: Risks to the fetus of anticoagulant therapy during pregnancy. Thromb Haemost 1989; 61:197 – 203.
80 Ben Ismail M, Abid F, Trabelsk S, Taktak M, Fekih M: Cardiac valve prostheses, anticoagulation, and pregnancy. Br Heart J 1986;55:101 – 105.
81 Braun S, Roberts A, Chamorro G, Leontic E, Casanegra P, Albuquerque J: Riesgo materno y fetal del embarazo en cardiopatas con y sin tratamiento anticoagulante. Rev Méd Chile 1984;112: 1009 – 1016.
82 Chong MKB, Harvey D, DeSwiet M: Follow-up study of children whose mothers were treated with warfarin during pregnancy. Br J Obstet Gynaecol 1984;91:1070 – 1073.
83 Lee PK, Wang RYC, Chow JSF, Cheung KL, Wong VCW, Chan TK: Combined use of warfarin and adjusted subcutaneous heparin during pregnancy in patients with an artificial heart valve. J Am Coll Cardiol 1986;8:221 – 224.
84 Matorras R, Reque JA, Usandizaga JA, Minguez JA, Larrea JL, Núñez L: Prosthetic heart valve and pregnancy. A study of 59 cases. Gynecol Obstet Invest 1985;19:21 – 31.
85 Parankumar P, Venugopal P, Kaul U, Iyer KS, Das B, Sampathkumar A, Airon B, Rao IM, Sharma ML, Bhatta ML, Gopinath N: Pregnancy in patients with prosthetic cardiac valve. Scand J Thorac Cardiovasc Surg 1988;22:19 – 22.

Richard M Pauli, MD, PhD
Clinical Genetics Center
Room 353
1500 Highland Avenue
University of Wisconsin - Madison
Madison, WI 53705 (USA)

Original Paper

Dev Brain Dysfunct 1993;6:248 – 265

1019 – 5815/93/0065 – 0248$2.75/0

Alcohol Embryopathy: Experience in 200 Patients

Frank Majewski

Institute of Human Genetics, Düsseldorf, FRG

Key Words. Alcohol embryopathy · Clinical symptoms · Frequency · Pathogenesis

Abstract. At present alcohol embryopathy (AE) is the most common recognizable cause of mental and growth retardation in children. In 200 children the severity of AE was graded from I to III according to the dysmorphologic appearance. Internal malformations, mental and statomotor development, as well as maternal history of alcohol consumption correlated to the relative degree of AE phenotype. A positive correlation was found between the degree of AE and the frequency of congenital heart defects (9% in AE I, 19% in AE II and 63% in AE III), other internal malformations such as genitourinary malformations, and the degree of mental retardation. The stage of maternal alcohol illness but not the daily (mostly excessive) maternal alcohol consumption influenced significantly the degree of AE. All mothers of children with AE suffered from alcohol illness. The frequency of AE among the offspring was also related to the increasing stage of maternal alcohol illness. In the critical stage there were 21%, and in the chronical stage 41% of the children affected with AE. The pathogenesis of AE is still unclear, but prevention by successful withdrawal treatment is possible, as some healthy children of formerly addicted mothers with affected children have shown.

Introduction

Alcohol embryotoxicity in humans has been reported since more than 2 decades. The teratogenic damage can vary from minimal cerebral disturbances to severe mental and morphological damage. The term alcohol effects describes mild behavioral and mental disturbances. The combination of growth retardation, dysmorphias/malformations and mental retardation is called fetal alcohol syndrome or alcohol embryopathy (AE). We prefer the term AE.

Alcohol Effects

Streissguth et al. [1] prospectively examined 500 children. Two hundred and fifty of their mothers had consumed alcohol moderately to heavily during pregnancy, and 250 few or nothing. Newborns of mothers who drank more than 1 oz daily (29.6 g) during pregnancy showed delayed reactions to stimuli with light, rattle and bell. At the age of 8 months and 4 years these children had some behavioral disturbances, especially attentional deficiency. Mentally subnormal children were only observed among offspring of mothers who consumed more than 2 oz (59 g) absolute alcohol per day during pregnancy. At a mean age of 7.5 years all 482 reexamined children were healthy, but there was a decrease in IQ by 7 points among 30 children whose mothers had consumed more than 1 oz per day.

Alcohol Embryopathy

The effects of mild or moderate alcohol consumption during pregnancy on the offspring are mild and often hard to verify. In contrast, alcohol illness and excessive alcohol abuse can cause severe physical and psychological damage in children, which is termed AE. Main symptoms of AE are pre- and postnatal growth retardation, microcephaly, mental retardation, hyperactivity, a characteristic face and some internal malformations. The diagnosis of AE can be assumed if all or most of these characteristics as well as a history of severe maternal alcohol abuse during pregnancy are present, and other syndromes with intrauterine growth retardation and microcephaly, in particular de Lange syndrome and Dubowitz syndrome, are excluded.

Frequency of AE

AE in the past and present time is the most frequent recognizable damage in children caused by a teratogenic drug. The incidence varied from 1:212 (France) [2] to 1:600 (Sweden) [3] or 1:700 (Seattle/USA) [4]. In Indian Reservations, incidence ranged from 1:97 to 1:750 live births [5]. The highest reported prevalence was 1:8 in a Canadian-Indian village [6].

In three centers in Germany more than 500 affected children are known [7 – 9].

Material and Methods

In a retrospective study 200 affected children were examined by the same investigator between 1974 and 1991. Most of the children were ascertained at the University Children's Hospitals of Tübingen, Mainz and Düsseldorf, FRG. Some other children were examined at the Institute of Human Genetics, Düsseldorf. The age at first examination varied from 1 day to 13 years, the majority of children was examined several times, the eldest patient was 18 years old. Statomotor and mental development was judged by Denver score, some children were examined by psychologists with various psychometric methods, especially the Kramer or Hawik test. Growth parameters were compared to normal data of Kunze and Murken [10] and Nellhaus [11].

Severity of AE was mainly graded according to dysmorphic features. In most children with AE III diagnosis could be deduced from the characteristic phenotype alone. Children with AE II or I were diagnosed by a maternal history of severe alcohol abuse during pregnancy, and exclusion of other syndromes associated with intrauterine growth retardation and microcephaly. The stage of maternal alcohol illness was judged according to the questionnaire by Jellinek [12].

Results and Discussion

Classification

The degree of prenatal damage is variable. Although there is a continuum from severe to mild damage, a classification into three degrees of severity is meaningful for prognosis [13].

AE III. The severe type is characterized by

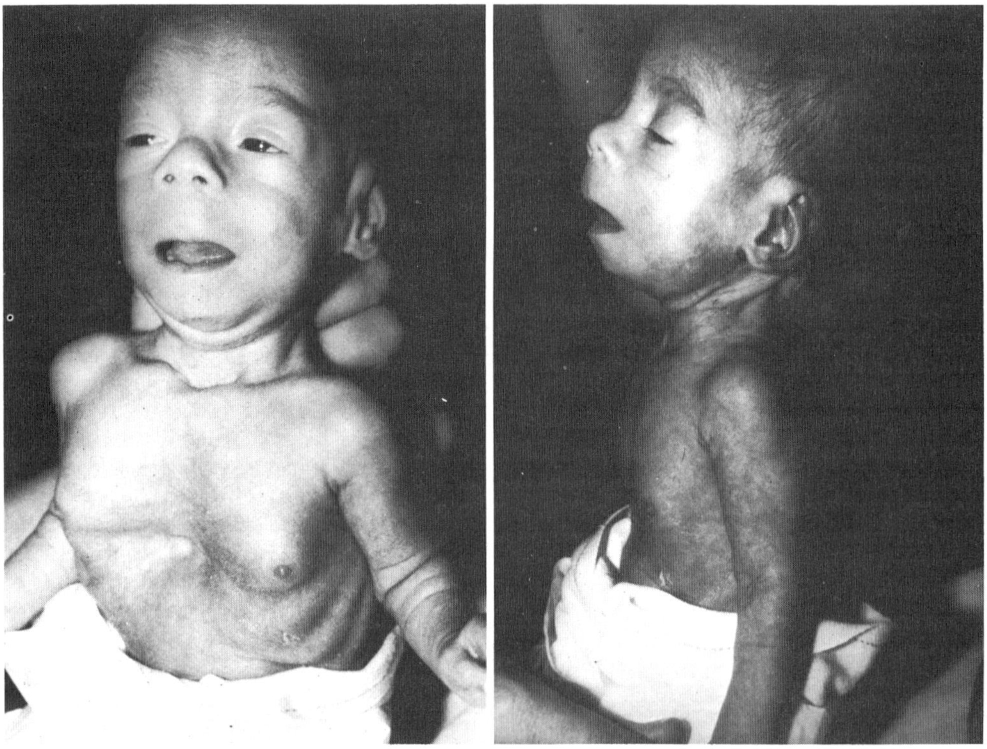

a b

Fig. 1. a Face of a newborn with AE III (case No. 181). **b** Profile of patient No. 181.

marked pre- and postnatal growth retardation, microcephaly, and mental retardation. The face is very typical, so that diagnosis of maternal alcoholism during pregnancy can be deduced. The forehead is rounded, there may be blepharophimosis, the nose is short and upturned, the philtrum is flat, the vermilion border of the lips is very narrow, the mandible is hypoplastic. Children with AE III frequently suffer from internal malformations (cf. below). Mental impairment is always severe, and most children are hypotonic and hyperactive (fig. 1, 2).

AE II. Patients with the moderate type have growth retardation as well as microcephaly. Their mental retardation is not as severe as in degree III. The face is dysmorphic, but without proven maternal alcoholism the diagnosis can be suspected only. However, hyperactivity and muscular hypotonia may be of diagnostic help (fig. 3). Internal malformations are not as frequent as in AE III.

AE I. The mild form is characterized by pre- and postnatal growth retardation, underweight and microcephaly. Mental development is normal or only slightly subnormal. The face is grossly normal, and there are few or no internal malformations. The diagnosis is only possible by a maternal history of severe alcoholism (fig. 4).

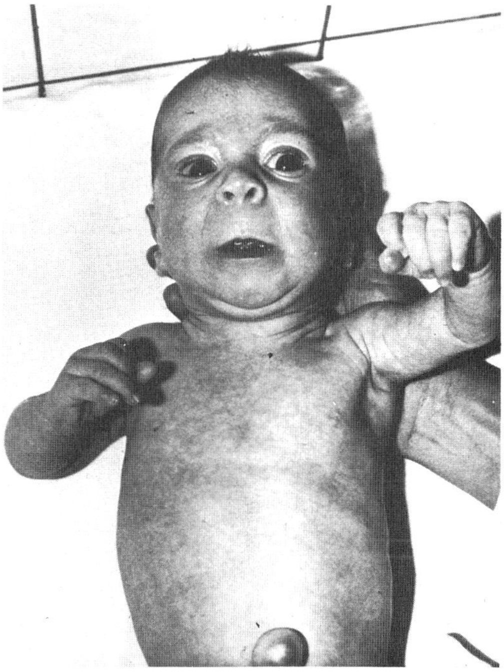

Fig. 2. Aspect of a baby with AE III.

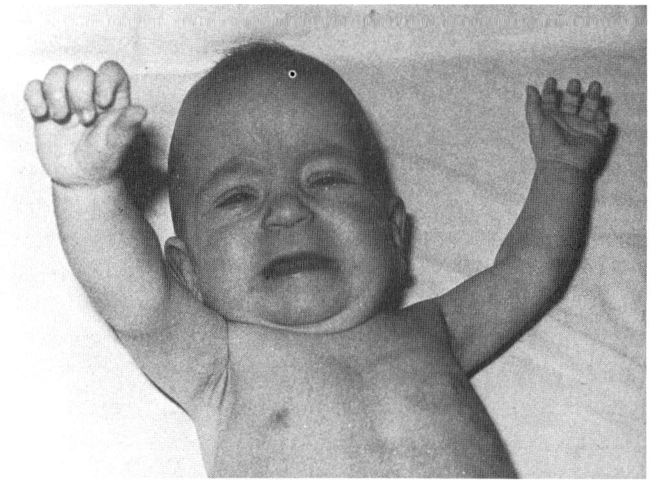

Fig. 3. Aspects of a child with AE II.

Frequency of Symptoms

In table 1 the frequencies of 34 common symptoms of 200 children with different degrees of AE are listed. In the left column every symptom was scored subjectively on a scale from 1 to 4, only extremely severe brain damage was graded as 8. The sum of each case allowed a comparable classification, given at

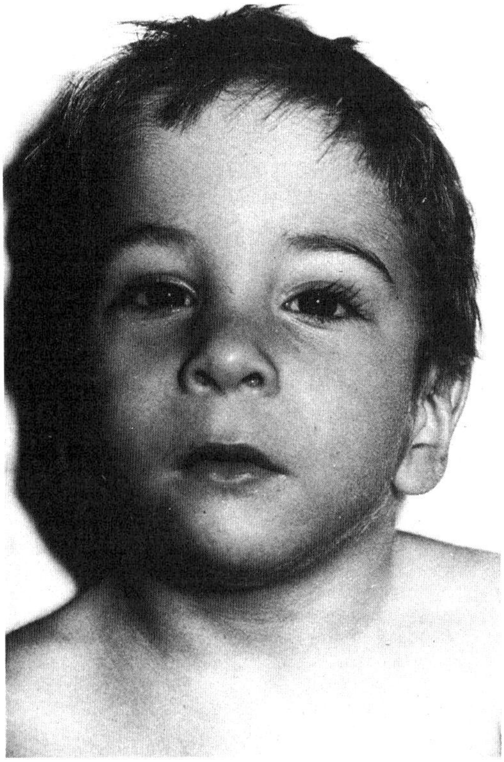

Fig. 4. Face of a child with AE I.

the bottom. It should be emphasized that this scoring system is not a diagnostic tool for AE (e.g. a child with de Lange syndrome can easily reach a score of AE III).

Most cases demonstrated intrauterine and postnatal growth retardation. About 80% were microcephalic and mentally retarded. Twenty-seven percent of all cases suffered from congenital heart defects, such as transposition of great vessels, pentalogy of Fallot and aplasia of one lung artery, but most common were septal defects [45]. The frequency of congenital heart defects was related to the degree of AE: 63% in patients with AE III, 19% in those with AE II, and 9% in patients with AE I. Forty percent exhibited mostly minor anomalies of external genitalia, at least 8% suffered from malformations of the genitourinary tract (diverticulas of bladder, hypoplastic kidney, polycystic kidney, megaureter, and hydronephrosis). Genitourinary malformations also correlated with the degree of AE: 58% in children with AE III, 38% in AE II, and 27% in AE I.

We observed tortuosity of retinal vessels in about 10%. Strabism and myopia were observed frequently. Significant hypoplasia of optic nerve disc was found in only 1 patient (case No. 200). Strömland [14] observed ocular involvement, e.g. myopia, strabism, hypoplasia of optic nerve disc and increased tortuosity of retinal vessels, in nearly 90% of her patients.

Frequency of symptoms according to the different degrees of AE are given in table 2. Though the classification of AE was initially based on dysmorphic criteria, it appeared that nearly all clinical features were more frequent in AE III than in AE II, and were rare in AE I. Except for cleft palate, genitourinary malformations and spina bifida, all features were also observed in cases with AE I, but less frequent and mostly of milder degrees than in cases with AE II or III. In cases with AE II the frequencies of nearly all symptoms are between those of AE III and I (for more detailed clinical description and literature review see [9]).

Anatomical and Functional CNS Findings

Our case No. 181 with AE III (fig. 1) died from congenital heart defect (atrial and ventricular septal defect) at the age of 8 months. Neuropathological examination revealed marked hydrocephalus internus et externus and agenesis of corpus callosum. A similar spectrum of malformations was observed by Clarren et al. [15, case 1]. There are only 16

Table 1. Characteristics in 200 patients with AE

Points	Symptoms	a	b	Frequency, %
4	Intrauterine growth retardation	149	178	83
–	Postnatal growth retardation	156	182	86
4	Microcephaly	153	194	79
2/4/8	Statomotor/mental retardation	121	148	82
4	Hyperactivity	140	190	74
2	Muscular hypotonia	105	185	57
2	Epicanthic folds	98	195	50
2	Ptosis	54	191	28
2	Blepharophimosis	50	182	27
–	Antimong. palpebral fissures	57	182	31
–	Strabism	33	166	20
–	Dysplastic ears	51	164	31
3	Short upturned nose	95	187	51
1	Nasolabial furrows	129	192	67
1	Small lips	126	195	65
4	Cleft palate	12	197	6
2	High arched palate	50	188	27
	Hypoplasia of maxilla	5	182	3
2	Hypoplasia of mandible	130	199	65
3	Anomalous palmar creases	128	192	67
2	Brachyclinodactyly V	74	195	38
2	Camptodactyly	25	195	13
1	Hypoplasia of endphalanges	26	188	14
2	Limited supination	20	187	11
2	Hip dislocation	19	173	11
–	Flat feet	55	131	42
–	Pectus excavatum	36	176	20
–	Pectus carinatum	13	171	8
4	Congenital heart defect	52	190	27
–	Hemangiomas	26	175	15
2/4	Genital anomalies	77	193	40
1	Sacral dimple	94	183	51
2	Hernias	19	163	12
4	Genitourinary malformations	12	151	8

AE I (n = 70): 10–29 points, AE II (n = 72): 30–39 points; AE III (n = 58): $\geqslant$40 points. a = Symptom observed; b = symptom looked for.

Table 2. Frequencies of symptoms in children with AE I (n = 70), AE II (n = 72), and AE III (n = 58)

Symptoms	AE III			AE II			AE I		
	a	b	%	a	b	%	a	b	%
Intrauterine growth retardation	49	52	94	50	62	81	50	64	78
Postnatal growth retardation	49	50	98	57	66	86	50	66	75
Microcephaly	47	53	89	56	72	78	50	69	72
Statomotor/mental retardation	34	35	97	48	53	90	39	60	65
Hyperactivity	45	52	86	58	71	81	37	67	55
Muscular hypotonia	38	51	75	39	70	56	28	64	44
Epicanthic folds	31	56	55	39	71	55	28	68	41
Ptosis	27	53	51	17	70	24	10	68	15
Blepharophimosis	16	51	31	28	68	41	6	63	10
Antimong. palpebral fissures	29	55	53	15	63	24	13	64	20
Strabism	12	45	27	13	62	21	8	59	14
Dysplastic ears	21	50	42	20	54	37	10	60	17
Short upturned nose	37	55	67	33	62	53	25	70	36
Nasolabial furrows	48	54	89	44	70	63	37	68	54
Small lips	44	55	80	50	72	69	32	68	47
Cleft palate	9	57	16	3	70	4	0	70	0
High arched palate	25	55	45	15	65	23	10	68	15
Hypoplasia of maxilla	1	50	2	2	65	3	2	67	3
Hypoplasia of mandible	53	58	91	56	71	79	21	70	30
Anomalous palmar creases	46	53	68	51	72	70	31	67	46
Brachyclinodactyly V	28	56	50	29	71	41	17	68	25
Camptodactyly	14	53	26	8	72	11	3	70	4
Hypoplasia of endphalanges	15	52	29	6	72	14	5	64	8
Limited supination	10	46	22	5	72	7	5	69	7
Hip dislocation	5	42	12	7	64	11	7	67	10
Flat feet	13	39	33	26	42	62	16	50	32
Pectus excavatum	7	43	16	13	67	20	16	66	24
Pectus carinatum	5	46	11	4	61	7	4	64	6
Congenital heart defect	33	52	63	13	69	19	6	69	9
Hemangiomas	13	52	25	7	61	11	6	62	10
Genital anomalies	31	53	58	27	71	38	19	69	27
Sacral dimple	33	50	66	37	70	53	24	63	38
Hernias	10	46	22	3	52	6	6	65	9
Genitourinary malformations	7	40	18	5	46	11	0	65	0

a = Symptom observed; b = symptom looked for.

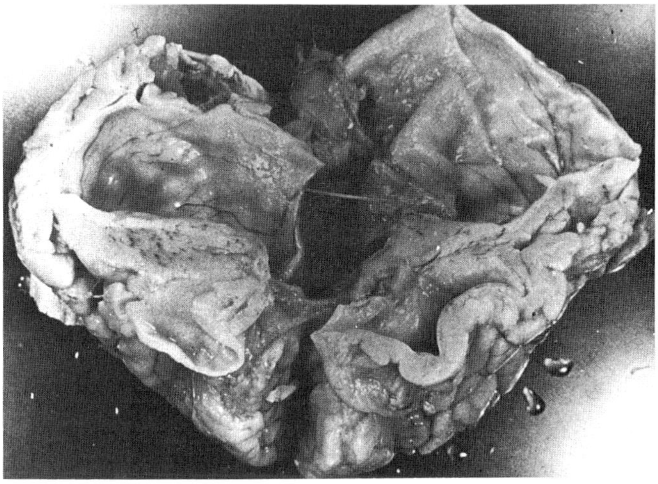

Fig. 5. Hydrocephalus internus et externus, porencephaly and agenesis of corpus callosum in patient No. 19 with AE III.

published brain dissections [15–20]. The malformations observed ranged from microdysplasias and heterotopias (10/16 cases) to severe brain malformations (5/16). These malformations included hydrocephalus internus (3 cases) [15, 18], hypoplasia of cerebellum (4 cases) [15, 18, 20], and agenesis of corpus callosum (3 cases) [15, 18, 20]. The severest malformations were observed in our case No. 18 [18]: agenesis of corpus callosum, hypoplasia of cerebellum, hydrocephalus internus et externus and a porencephalic cyst (fig. 5). In a few cases holoprosencephaly as a possible pathogenic consequence of heavy maternal alcohol abuse has been reported [21, 22].

Four children suffered from neural tube defects. The frequency of spina bifida in our series was 2%; this is a twentyfold increase compared to the general population. Friedman [23] also suggested that the frequency of neural tube defects in children with AE is increased. Figure 6 shows a newborn with AE III, severe congenital heart defect and spina bifida.

Ten percent of our patients suffered from convulsions. Seventy-four percent demonstrated hyperexcitability, hyperactivity and ataxia. In most children these symptoms decreased after the age of 2–3 years. Muscular hypotonia was observed in 57% of our cases. The degree of mental retardation was related to the physical abnormalities in the children. The medium IQ of cases with degree III was 66, of cases with degree II 79 and of cases with degree I 91 (table 3).

A similar correlation of morphological abnormalities and mental retardation was observed by Streissguth et al. [24] in 20 cases. In a follow-up study of 8 children the mean initial IQ of these children was 56, and 10 years later 61 [25]. Löser and Ilse [26] followed 22 patients aged 14–20 years with AE of different degrees over several years. Four patients were able to attend a regular school, 2 went to a school for children with learning disabilities, 2 to a special school for children with physical handicaps, 9 to a school for the mentally handicapped, one patient was unable to attend any school. All 7 cases with AE III

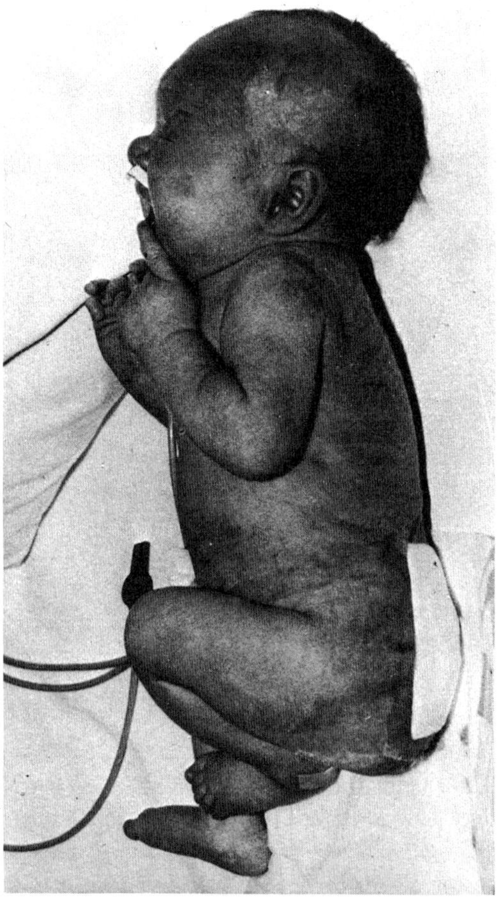

Fig. 6. A newborn with AE III with cardiac defect and spina bifida (case No. 176).

attended a school for the mentally handicapped.

Streissguth et al. [27] reexamined 32 adolescents and adults with AE. The mean age was 18 years (range 12 – 40 years). The average IQ of these patients was 66 (range 30 – 90). Deficits in arithmetics were most characteristic. Maladaptive behaviors such as poor judgement, distructibility and difficulty perceiving social cues were common. None of the adults was able to live on her/his own.

Table 3. IQ (Kramer) in 18 patients with AE

AE III		AE II		AE I	
age years	points	age years	points	age years	points
5.2	50	5	84	7.7	93
4.5	70	4.6	85	4.5	70
3.7	63	6.3	102	7	86
5.2	50	6.3	47	5	105
8	95			4.7	130
				7	92
				6	61
				8.8	127
				4.8	65

AE III: n = 5, mean = 66.6; AE II: n = 4, mean = 79.5; AE I: n = 9, mean = 91.6.
Mean (n = 18) = 82.

Auxological Data

The mean birthweight of 112 cases with AE born at term was 2,355 g. This weight corresponds to the 50th percentile of children born in week 34.5 of gestation. Mean head circumference and length were similarly retarded by 3 – 3.5 weeks. In most newborns with AE there was a proportionate retardation of all three parameters and no relative microcephaly (table 4). There was a decrease in the mean values of weight, length and head circumference from degree I to degree II to degree III (table 5).

In figure 7 measurements are given in standard deviation scores (SDS). At birth there was a deviation of all parameters by more than 3 SDS. During the first 6 months there was a decrease in weight and even more in head circumference to about – 4 SDS. From the second month onwards there was some catch-up on height, from the sixth month on weight and from the twelfth month on head cir-

Table 4. Weight, lenght and head circumference (OFC) in 112 children with AE born at term

	mean weight, g	mean lenght, cm	mean OFC, cm
	2,355	45.99	31.9
Corresponding week of gestation	34.5	34.5	35

Table 5. Data of 112 children with AE I, II and III born at term

	mean weight, g		mean lenght, cm		mean OFC, cm	
	m	f	m	f	m	f
AE I (n = 38)	2,550	2,676	48.1	48.1	33.0	33.1
AE II (n = 44)	2,345	2,335	45.9	46.0	31.9	31.4
AE III (n = 30)	2,101	1,954	44.1	43.9	31.6	30.8

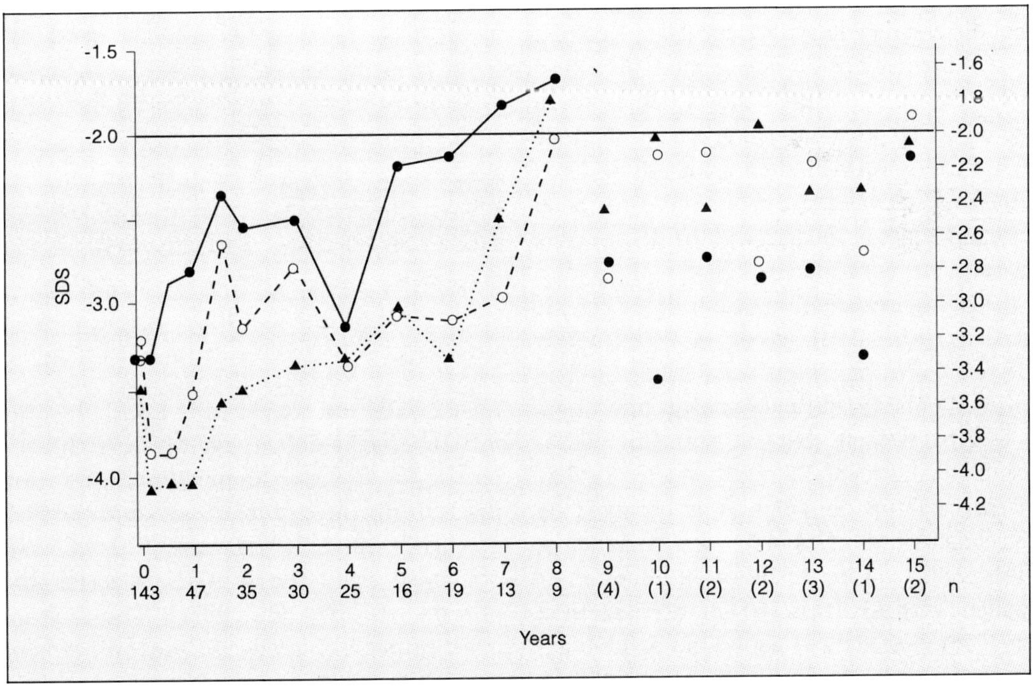

Fig. 7. Growth data of 175 children with AE, given in SDS. • = Height; ○ = weight; ▲ = head circumference.

Table 6. Mean measurements of children with AE I, II and III given in SDS

	Weight	Height	OFC
AE I	−2.54	−2.01	−2.71
AE II	−3.23	−2.88	−3.57
AE III	−3.89	−3.58	−4.14

OFC = Head circumference.

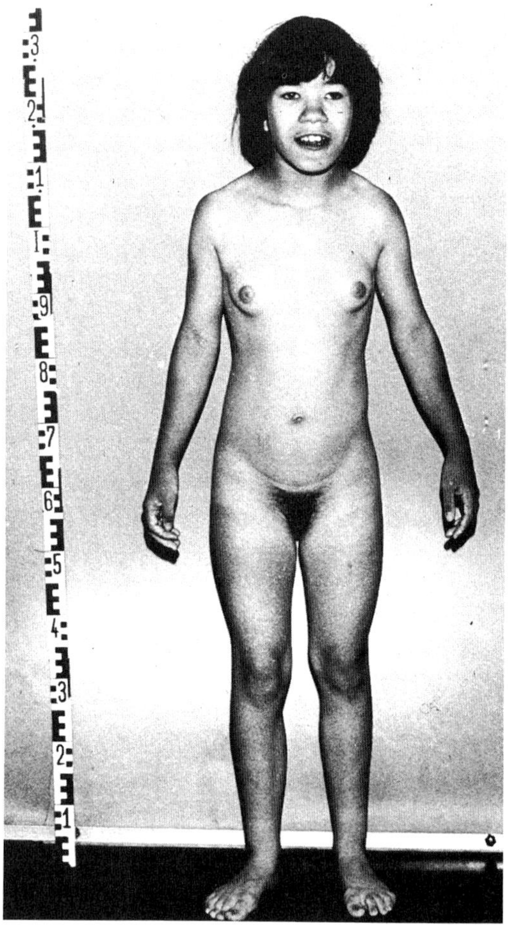

Fig. 8. A girl with AE III at the age of 14 years.

cumference. In all age groups (except newborns) head circumference was the most retarded parameter.

At age 6.5 years height increased over the 3rd percentile, at 8 years head circumference followed and weight nearly came up to the −2-SD line. For the age groups '9 years and older' the numbers of data are too small for statistical analysis. In this graph the data are not differentiated for the three degrees of AE.

Comparison of the mean values in SDS of all age groups (table 6) shows that children with AE III are more retarded in all three parameters than children with AE II or I. Retardation was most pronounced for head circumference in children with AE III reaching a value of more than −4 SDS.

The last examination of our oldest female patient with AE III was at an age of nearly 18 years. Her final height was 145 cm. She had normal puberty, normal female proportions, slight overweight, but she was still microcephalic and mentally retarded (fig. 8). The same catch-up on weight was observed by Streissguth et al. [25] in her female patients. The predicted final height of our oldest male patient with AE III is 160 cm. Streissguth et al. [27] reported on 31 adolescent or adult patients with AE. The mean growth retardation corresponded to −2.1 SD (range −6 to 0 SD), head circumference to −1.9 SD (range −5 to +2 SD), and weight to −1.4 SD (−4 to 0 SD). Weight deficiency, which is characteristic for young children with AE, was less marked in these adolescents and adults. Twenty-five percent of the cases with AE were not underweight. The mean weight-height proportion was 48% (3– 90%). The time of onset of puberty in all cases was within normal limits.

Facial appearance changed with age. In elder cases the nose is no more short and up-

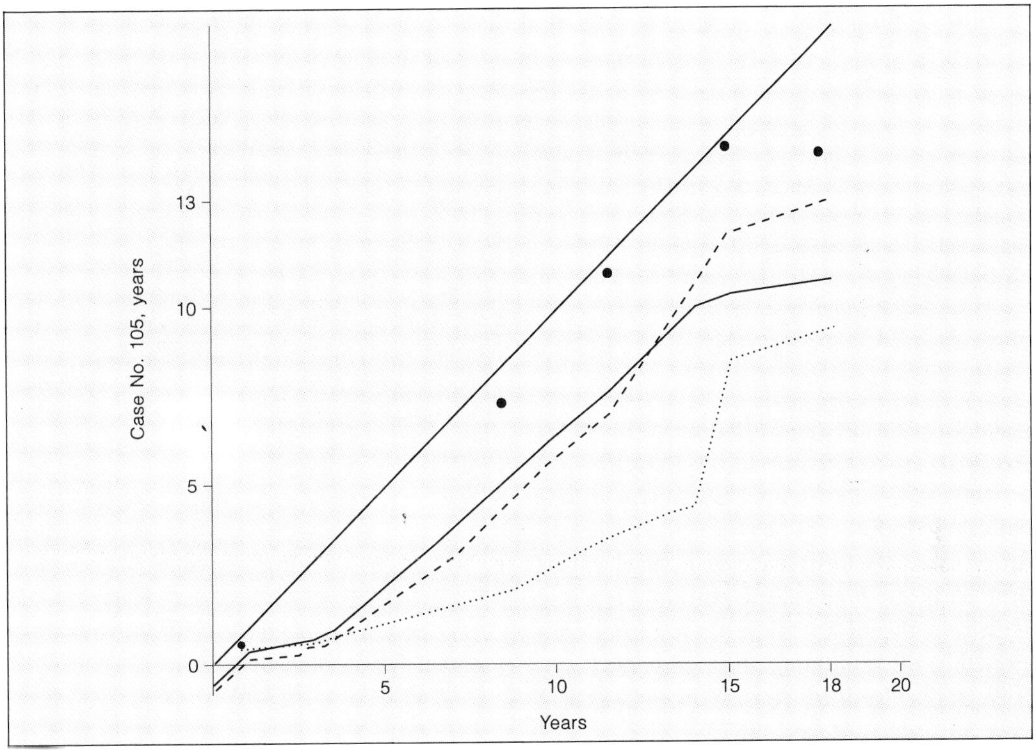

Fig. 9. Growth data of an individual case with AE III (case of fig. 8). • = Corpal bone age; --- = weight; – = height; ··· = head circumference.

turned, the lips are no longer thin and the chin often becomes rather prominent (fig. 8). The same changes of facial appearance were noted by Streissguth et al. [25, 27]. The only unchanged feature in both populations were small palpebral fissures and microcephaly. In elder cases photos of the baby age are often a necessary diagnostic tool.

In figure 9 the development of carpal bone age, weight, height and head circumference of the individual case of figure 8 with AE III is given. Carpal bone age was nearly normal. As in the adolescent female American cases after age 12 years, weight gain was faster than height gain. Typically, the most impaired parameter is head circumference. From a clinical point of view this observation suggests that it should not be recommended to force feeding before puberty.

Correlation of Weight with Head Circumference

Except for severe congenital heart defects, microcephaly and mental retardation are the main problems for most children with AE. To improve head growth and corresponding brain weight is an important goal of medical care in children with AE. Brain growth velocity has its maximum between the 32nd gestational week and the 6th month after the normal date

Table 7. Correlation of weight and head circumference (OFC) of 175 children in SDS

	OFC in		
	AE I	AE II	AE III
Weight			
≥ −2 SDS	−1.86	−1.96	–
< −2 SDS	−3.14	−3.87	−4.11

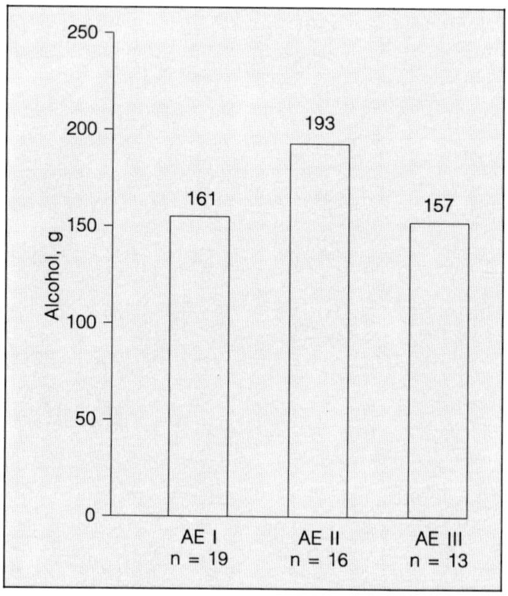

Fig. 10. Correlation between degree of AE and maternal alcohol consumption.

of birth. After the age of 19 months the brain weight velocity decreases to less than 10%. In a group of 27 otherwise healthy small-for-date children, Brandt [28] has published a catch-up on head circumference to normal values after early and high-caloric postnatal feeding. However, this observation has not been confirmed by other authors, and is discussed controversially. In order to study whether there was an influence of weight on head circumference, patients with AE I, II and III were divided into two main weight groups: ≥ −2 SDS or < −2 SDS (table 7). Children with AE I in general had less pronounced microcephaly than those with AE II or III. Heavier children above −2 SDS with AE I and AE II had markedly larger head circumferences than children below −2 SDS. This may reflect some correlation of weight and brain growth. However, these differences are nearly the same at birth, and in heavier children no more catch-up on head circumference is observed than in the underweight children. Thus our patients with higher weight do not have a better brain growth. Nevertheless attempts should be made to increase head circumference by early and high-caloric feeding, especially in the first 6 months of life. Increased head circumference parallels with increased brain growth [28] and probably better mental development due to a better myelinization, better growth of dendrites and increased formation of synapses.

Pathogenesis

All mothers of our patients with AE were alcohol addicted. We and Löser et al. [29] have never seen a child with AE after social drinking or even binge drinking. Streissguth et al. [30] observed psychological disturbances after prenatal exposure to binge drinking, but no case with AE. We are often asked by pediatricians to examine children of mothers who had more or less alcohol abuse during pregnancy. In no case, except for maternal alcohol addiction, we noticed features of AE. Most of the mothers with children suffering from AE drunk more than 150 g absolute alcohol per day during pregnancy. Mothers of children with AE III had no higher daily

Table 8. Degree of AE among the offspring (n = 72) in relation to the stage of maternal alcohol illness

	Prodromal	Critical	Chronical
AE I	1	15	9
AE II	–	10	12
AE III	–	7	18

Table 9. AE in 28 siblings

Family	Siblings	AE I–III	elder → younger
Li.	I	II	
Ha.	I	II	III
Sp.	I	II	III
Ci.	I	II	
Ko.	I	I	
Fe.	I	II	
Ba.	I	II	
Be.	III	III	
Rö.	I	I	
Cr.	I	II	
Da.	I	II	
Eb.	II	III	
Fa.	I	II	

alcohol intake in the first trimester than mothers of children with AE I (fig. 10). Löser et al. [29] reported on 8 children prenatally exposed to excessive amounts of alcohol (more than 180 g per day). One child exhibited no disturbances, 3 children presented with alcohol effects, and 4 with a very mild degree of AE. Löser et al. concluded that the degree of AE or the severity of disturbance in the outcome does not depend on the amounts of alcohol. Forty-three mothers of children with AE I, the mild form of AE, consumed an average amount of 175.5 g alcohol per day during pregnancy. This is nearly the same amount as in 13 mothers of children with AE I investigated by us who consumed an average amount of 157 g alcohol per day (fig. 10).

In 72 mothers we could classify the stage of alcohol illness according to Jellinek [12]. In the prodromal stage alcohol intake is excessive, but there is no loss of control. With the loss of control drinkers are in the critical stage which leads to psychological and physical dependence. In the chronical stage mothers drink compulsively and begin drinking in the morning. This stage leads to organic illness and psychosis, and to psychological and physical ruin. Mothers in the chronical stage during pregnancy had significantly more children with AE III than those in the critical stage, and mothers in the critical stage had significantly more children with AE I than those in the chronical stage (table 8). In the prodromal stage only 1 child was born with mild AE.

This correlation of maternal stage of alcohol illness and degree of damage in the offspring is supported by our observations in 28 siblings. Most times the younger sib was more severely impaired than the older one (table 9). From our study it is evident that extremely high daily alcohol intake and an increased stage of maternal alcohol illness are prerequisits for AE. Hanson et al. [4] and some other authors suggested that moderate alcohol intake during pregnancy and social drinking can cause embryonic damage. However, the 2 children in their study who exhibited symptoms of AE were born to heavily alcoholic mothers. Sulaiman et al. [31] examined 952 consecutive primigravidas in Scotland, and correlated the maternal alcohol intake with the perinatal outcome. Before pregnancy more than 90% consumed alcohol, and 53% smoked. In the first 4 months of pregnancy the proportion of alcohol-consuming women decreased to 57% and that of smoking women to 44%. There was no negative influence on the newborn, if the mothers consumed less than 14 g alcohol per day during pregnancy. Among the newborns of mothers who consumed 14 – 17 g daily, there was a decrease of birthweight by 109 g, and of head circumference by 13 mm (not significant). There was a significant decrease of weight, length, head circumference and Apgar scores among the newborns of mothers who drank more than 17 g per day (without an upper limit). However, after correction with respect to smoking, social class, maternal height and other variables, only the decrease of Apgar scores (– 0.23 points) and duration of gestation (– 2 weeks) remained significant. Plant [32] published a large prospective study of 1,008 pregnant women who gave birth to 1,012 children. Only 8% of these mothers lived abstinent. The others (92%) drank alcohol during pregnancy, but mostly moderately. Of these 4.7% drank 10 or more units (1 unit = 1 cl = 7.9 g) per day. Despite of a highly sophisticated examination of the pregnant women and their children, Plant was unable to observe a child with AE. This is not in contradiction to our observations: there is only a major risk of the offspring if the mother is alcohol addicted and drinks excessively during pregnancy. Larsson et al. [33] prospectively examined and followed 40 children, who were all prenatally exposed to various amounts of alcohol. The children of women with chronic alcohol illness exhibited significant growth retardation. Three out of 6 children prenatally exposed to excessive amounts presented with symptoms of AE. None of the children of mothers who stopped drinking during pregnancy exhibited growth retardation or symptoms of AE. But 12 out of 13 children of alcoholic mothers suffered from psychological or behavioral disturbances, even if the mother reduced or stopped alcohol abuse during pregnancy. We examined 27 children of 24 mothers who asked for genetic counselling because of alcohol problems during pregnancy. These mothers mostly asked for termination of the pregnancy, which was recommended in no case. Nearly all mothers reduced their alcohol intake after genetic counselling. All 24 children of the nonaddicted mothers and 1 child of a mother in the critical stage of alcohol illness were healthy. Two mothers in the critical stage gave birth to children with AE I and II, respectively. The latter child exhibited no intrauterine growth retardation, possibly due to maternal abstinence during the second and third trimester of pregnancy. From these observations one might hypothesize that some secondary factors related to alcohol illness may increase embryonic damage, e.g. hypoglycemia, elevated levels of acetaldehyde [34], methanol [35], deficiencies of zinc, vitamins or folate. Tanaka et al. [36] demonstrated in rats that supplementation with zinc and Vitamin E during pregnancies with alcohol exposition can decrease embryonic damage (for further discussion on the pathogenesis see [8, 37, 38]).

Frequency of AE among the Offspring

In two further studies we examined 81 children of 69 mothers, who had undergone a withdrawal treatment [39] (the affected 20 children were included in the total of 200 cases). All mothers had been alcohol addicted before and during pregnancy. From these studies we learned that the frequency of AE among the offspring is influenced by the stage of maternal alcohol illness. In the prodromal stage only one child exhibited mild symptoms of AE. In the critical stage 21% and in the chronical stage 41% of the offspring had symptoms of AE (fig. 11). Similar as demon-

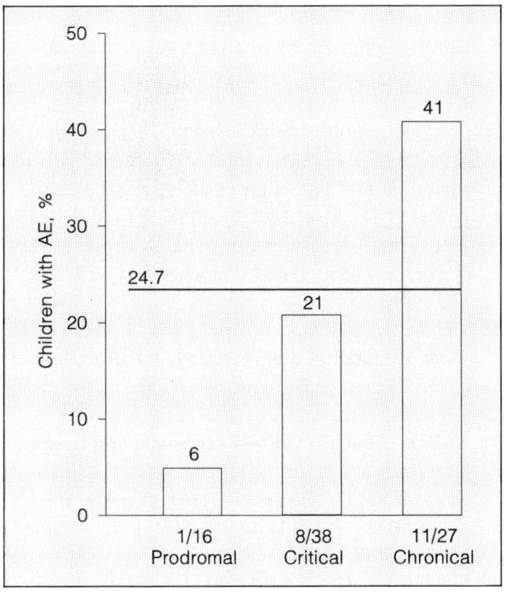

Fig. 11. Frequency of AE in relation to the stage of maternal alcohol illness.

strated in table 8, there were higher degrees of AE in the chronical stage than in the critical stage.

In the literature there are no similar studies. Only Jones et al. [40] in USA and Halliday et al. [41] in Ireland studied the frequencies of AE among offsprings of chronically or heavily alcoholic mothers. Both observed a frequency of 43% of children with AE. Summing up all comparable studies, 42.3% of offspring of mothers with chronic alcohol illness suffered from AE (table 10). Since all three studies [40–42] came to similar results, this percentage seems to be realistic.

Prevention

All available studies on the frequency of AE among the offspring resulted in 42%

Table 10. Frequency of AE among the offspring of chronic alcoholic women

Country	Frequency		Author
	%	n	
USA	43	10/23	Jones et al. [40]
Ireland	43	15/35	Halliday et al. [41]
Germany	41	11/27	Majewski et al. [42]
Total	42.3	36/85	

damaged children of chronic alcoholic mothers. From our study it is evident that the majority of these children are severely affected. From these studies and from the mostly very bad psychosocial familial background, termination of pregnancy seems to be justified in pregnant women with chronic alcohol illness [17]. A better method of prevention is information of the population and withdrawal treatment in alcoholic women [43]. Like in Huddinge [44] all pregnant women should be asked about their alcohol intake, and in case the pregnant woman has alcohol problems, treatment should be offered.

We were aware of 2 mothers who had children after successful withdrawal treatment. Before withdrawal, 1 mother was in the chronical stage and gave birth to a child with AE III, the other one was in the critical stage and also had a child with AE III. After withdrawal treatment both of them became pregnant again and gave birth to perfectly normal and healthy children.

References

1 Streissguth AP, Barr HM, Sampson PD: Moderate prenatal alcohol exposure: Effects on child IQ and learning problems at age 7.5 years. Alcohol Clin Exp Res 1990;14:662–669.

2 Dehaene P, Crépin G, Delahousse G, Querleu D, Walbaum R, Titran M, Samaille-Vilette C: Aspects epidémiologiques du syndrome d'alcoolisme foetal. 45 observations en 3 ans. Nouv Presse Méd 1981;10:2639 – 2643.
3 Olegard R, Sabel KG, Aronsson M, Sandin B, Johannsson PR, Carlsson C, Kyllerman M, Iversen K, Hrbek AS: Effects on the child of alcohol abuse during pregnancy. Retrospective and prospective studies. Acta Paediatr Scand Suppl 1979;275:112 – 121.
4 Hanson JW, Streissguth AP, Smith DW: The effects of moderate alcohol consumption during pregnancy on fetal growth and morphogenesis. J Pediatr 1978;92:457 – 460.
5 May PA, Hymbaugh KJ, Aase JM, Samet JM: Epidemiology of fetal alcohol syndrome among American Indians of the Southwest. Soc Biol 1983; 30:374 – 387.
6 Robinson GC, Conry JL, Conry RF: Clinical profile and prevalence of fetal alcohol syndrome in an isolated community in British Columbia. Can Med Assoc J 1987;137:203 – 207.
7 Löser H: Alkoholeffekte und Schwachformen der Alkoholembryopathie. Dtsch Ärztebl 1991;88: 1921 – 1929.
8 Spohr HL: Neurologische und psychiatrische Befunde bei pränataler Alkoholexposition; in Majewski F (ed): Die Alkoholembryopathie. Frankfurt, Umwelt und Medizin, 1987, pp 134 – 142.
9 Majewski F: Teratogene Schäden durch Alkohol; in Kisker KP, et al (eds): Psychiatrie der Gegenwart. Berlin, Springer, 1987, pp 243 – 272.
10 Kunze D, Murken J: Diagnostik von Längenalter und Gewichtsalter mit neuen Somatogrammen. Kinderarzt 1974;5:1077 – 1085.
11 Nellhaus G: Headcircumference from birth to eighteen years. Practical composite international and interracial graphs. Pediatrics 1968;41:106 – 114.
12 Jellinek EM: Phases in the drinking history of alcoholics: Analysis of a survey conducted by the official organ of AA. Q J Stud Alcohol 1946;7:1 – 88.
13 Majewski F, Bierich JR, Löser H, Michaelis R, Leiber B, Bettecken F: Zur Klinik und Pathogenese der Alkoholembryopathie (Bericht über 68 Patienten): Münch Med Wochenschr 1976;118: 1635 – 1642.
14 Strömland K: Ocular involvement in the fetal alcohol syndrome. Surv Ophthalmol 1987;31: 277 – 284.
15 Clarren SK, Alvord EC, Sumi SM, Streissguth AP, Smith DW: Brain malformations related to prenatal exposure to ethanol. J Pediatr 1978;92: 64 – 67.
16 Jones KL, Smith DW, Ulleland C, Streissguth AP: Pattern of malformations in offspring of chronic alcoholic mothers. Lancet 1973;i:1267 – 1271.
17 Majewski F, Fischbach H, Peiffer J, Bierich JR: Zur Frage der Interruptio bei alkoholkranken Frauen. Dtsch Med Wochenschr 1978;103: 895 – 898.
18 Peiffer J, Majewski F, Fischbach H, Bierich JR, Volk B: Alcohol embryopathy. Neuropathology of 3 children and 3 fetuses. J Neurol Sci 1979; 41:125 – 137.
19 Volk B: Klinisch-neuropathologische Befunde und experimentelle Untersuchungen zur Alkoholembryopathie; in Majewski F (ed): Die Alkoholembryopathie. Frankfurt, Umwelt und Medizin, 1987, pp 89 – 101.
20 Wisniewski K, Dambska M, Shev JH, Quazi Q: A clinical neuropathological study of the fetal alcohol syndrome. Neuropediatrics 1983;14: 197 – 201.
21 Bönnemann C, Meinecke P: Holoprosencephaly as a possible embryonic alcohol effect: Another observation. Am J Med Genet 1990;37:431 – 432.
22 Ronen GM, Andrews WL: Holoprosencephaly as a possible embryonic alcohol effect. Am J Med Genet 1991;40:151 – 154.
23 Friedman JM: Can maternal alcohol ingestion cause neural tube defects? J Pediatr 1982;101: 232 – 234.
24 Streissguth AP, Herman CS, Smith DW: Intelligence, behaviour and dysmorphogenesis in the fetal alcohol syndrome: A report on 20 patients. J Pediatr 1978;92:363 – 367.
25 Streissguth AP, Clarren SK, Jones KL: Natural history of the fetal alcohol syndrome: A 10-year follow-up of 11 patients. Lancet 1985;ii:85 – 91.
26 Löser H, Ilse R: Körperliche und geistige Lang zeitentwicklung bei Kindern mit Alkoholembryopathie. Sozialpädiatr Prax Klin 1991;13: 8 – 14.
27 Streissguth AP, Aase JM, Clarren SK, Randels SP, LaDue RA, Smith DF: Fetal alcohol syndrome in adolescents and adults. JAMA 1991;265: 1961 – 1967.
28 Brandt J: Kopfumfang und Gehirnentwicklung. Klin Wochenschr 1981;59:995 – 1007.

29 Löser H, Grävinghoff K, Rustemeyer P: Schwachformen der Alkoholembryopathie nach exzessivem Alkoholgenuβ. Monatsschr Kinderheilk 1989;37:764 – 769.
30 Streissguth AP, Bookstein FL, Sampson PD, Barr HM: Neurobehavioural effects of prenatal alcohol. Part III. Partial least squares analysis of neuropsychologic tests. Neurotoxicol Teratol 1989;11: 493 – 507.
31 Sulaiman ND, Flore EV, Taylor DJ, Ogston SA: Alcohol consumption in Dundee primigravidas and its effects on outcome of pregnancy. Br Med J 188;296:1500 – 1503.
32 Plant M: Women, drinking, and pregnancy. London, Tavistock Publication, 1985.
33 Larsson G, Bohlinger AB, Tunell R: Prospective study of children exposed to variable amounts of alcohol in utero. Arch Dis Child 1985;60: 316 – 321.
34 Véghelyi PV, Osztovics M, Kardos G, Leisztner L, Szaszovensky E, Igali S, Imrei J: The fetal alcohol syndrome: Symptoms and pathogenesis. Acta Paediatr Hung 1978;19:171 – 189.
35 Bonte W, Sprung R: Methanol and alcoholism; in Noordzij PC, Roszbach R (eds): Alcohol, Drugs and Traffic Safety. Amsterdam, Elsevier, 1987, pp 509 – 512.
36 Tanaka H, Nakazawa K, Suzuki N, Arima M: Prevention possibility for brain dysfunction in rat with the fetal alcohol syndrome – Low-zinc-status and hypoglycemia. Brain Dev 1982;4:429 – 438.
37 Henderson GJ, Patwardhan RV, Hoyumpa AM, Schenker S: Fetal alcohol syndrome: Overview of pathogenesis. Neurobehav Toxicol Teratol 1981; 3:73 – 80.
38 Majewski F: Alcohol embryopathy: Some facts and speculations about pathogenesis. Neurobehav Toxicol 1981;3:129 – 144.
39 Sokolowski F, Sokolowski A, Majewski P: Risiken für die Nachkommen alkoholkranker Frauen. Gynäkol Prax 1988;12:635 – 649.
40 Jones KL, Smith DW, Streissguth AP, Myrianthopoulos NC: Outcome in offspring of chronic alcoholic women. Lancet 1974;i;1076 – 1078.
41 Halliday HC, Reid MM, McClure G: Results of heavy drinking in pregnancy. Br J Obstet Gynaecol 1982;89:892 – 895.
42 Majewski F: Die Alkoholembryopathie – Eine häufige und vermeidbare Störung; in Majewski F (ed): Die Alkoholembryopathie. Frankfurt, Umwelt und Medizin, 1987, pp 109 – 123.
43 Little RE: Reducing fetal alcohol effects: The Seattle pregnancy and health program; in Majewski F (ed): Die Alkoholembryopathie. Frankfurt, Umwelt und Medizin, 1987, pp 197 – 203.
44 Larsson G: Program for early identification and treatment of pregnant abusers; in Majewski F (ed): Die Alkoholembryopathie. Frankfurt, Umwelt und Medizin, 1987, pp 189 – 196.
45 Löser H: Herzfehler und toxische Herzmuskelschäden bei Alkoholembryopathie; in Majewski F (ed): Die Alkoholembryopathie. Frankfurt, Umwelt und Medizin, 1987, pp 124 – 133.

Prof. Dr. Frank Majewski
Institute of Human Genetics
Moorenstrasse 5
D-W – 4000 Düsseldorf (FRG)

Dev Brain Dysfunct 1993;6:266–278

1019–5815/93/0065–0266$2.75/0

Teratogenicity of Carbamazepine: A Review of the Literature

Vibeke Vestermark

Department of Gynecology and Obstetrics, Herlev University Hospital, University of Copenhagen, Herlev, Denmark

Key Words. Carbamazepine · Teratogenesis · Birth defects · Anti-epileptic drugs

Abstract. Animal experiments have shown that carbamazepine (CBZ) has minor teratogenic effects. In human beings it is not possible to identify any specific teratogenic patterns related to exposure to CBZ in utero. Like other antiepileptic drugs CBZ may be associated with different minor anomalies. No correlation between CBZ and brain dysfunction has been established, but only few studies have yet dealt with this possibility. Exposure to CBZ in utero carries a small risk of spina bifida. Malformations are more frequent in children of epileptic mothers than in children of non-epileptic mothers. Monotherapy is less teratogenic than polytherapy. No anti-epileptic drug is absolutely safe, but CBZ is an agent with minor teratogenic effects.

Introduction

Generalized seizures during pregnancy can be extremely hazardous to the mother and her fetus [1]. Status epilepticus is a rare complication in pregnancy with high perinatal and maternal mortality [2]. Seizures pose a greater overall risk to the fetus than proper use of anti-epileptic drugs (AED) [3, 4].

In 1964, Janz and Fuchs [5] raised the question, 'Are anti-epileptic drugs harmful during pregnancy?' Since then, a large number of publications have dealt with this question.

Carbamazepine (CBZ) was synthesized in 1953 as part of a programme investigating analogues of chlorpromazine. Its anticonvulsant properties remained undetected for some years, and the first clinical study in epilepsy was not performed until 1963 [6]. CBZ was generally considered to be non-teratogenic and the drug of choice for women with child-bearing potential [7–9]. In 1979, in a review of the literature, Niebyl et al. [10] suggested that CBZ did not carry any teratogenic risk. In 1983, Bossi [11] wrote that there was no evidence that CBZ may be associated with malformations, but the data were scanty. In 1986, Robertson [12] stated that no AED seems free of teratogenic risk, but with the commonly used AED e.g. CBZ, the risk was relatively low and represented less potential harm to the fetus than seizures. In the light of their study, Jones et al. [13] in 1989 stated that CBZ itself is teratogenic.

Malformations in Children of Epileptic Mothers

A major malformation has surgical, medical or cosmetic importance, and minor anomalies do not [14]. Hypertelorism, strabismus, inner epicanthal folds, broad nasal bridge, low-set or abnormally formed ears, hypoplasia of the distal phalanges, and nail hypoplasia are examples of minor anomalies [15 – 17].

The overall frequency of major malformations in children born to mothers with epilepsy is about twice the rate of the normal populations [1, 11, 17 – 26]. Many studies have shown that there is a higher incidence of malformations in children of epileptic women taking anticonvulsants than in children of untreated mothers [15 – 17, 27 – 33]. The difference between the malformation rates in treated and untreated mothers may be due to a teratogenic effect of AED, or it may be due to the fact that untreated mothers differ from treated mothers (e.g. less severe epilepsy or less frequent seizures). Genetic factors too are involved in the teratogenic action of AED. Certain malformations, such as cleft lip and palate, are often familiar and presumably have a hereditary component.

Minor anomalies are also more frequent in children of epileptic mothers than in children of non-epileptic mothers [21, 34 – 36]. However, in some of the studies, no differences were observed between children of treated and those of untreated mothers [35, 36], or a difference was found only if the infants had been exposed to polytherapy [34]. Minor anomalies are more frequent after exposure to polytherapy compared with monotherapy [37, 38]. Clinical evaluation of minor anomalies is subjective and sensitive to observer bias. A reliable comparison between differently exposed groups is only possible in blinded studies.

Mental Function in Children of Epileptic Mothers

Children exposed to AED in utero are reported to have developmental delay, subnormal IQ, or learning disabilities more often than children of non-epileptic mothers [18, 22, 23, 38, 39]. However, these findings have not been confirmed in all studies [36, 40, 41]. To some extent, these apparent contradictions may be due to a lack of information of whether monotherapy or polytherapy has been applied. There is some evidence that polytherapy during pregnancy is more harmful to mental development than monotherapy [38, 39].

Pharmacokinetics

Most oral formulations of CBZ are well-absorbed with high bioavailability, and 70 – 80% of the drug is bound to proteins in plasma [42].

CBZ is metabolized in the liver by oxidation before excretion in the urine [42]. A major metabolite is CBZ 10,11-epoxide (CBZ-E). The plasma concentrations of CBZ-E are

10 – 50% of those of CBZ [42]. The CBZ-E metabolite not only contributes to the anticonvulsant and antineuralgic properties, but it also has a neurotoxic side effect [6, 43]. CBZ-E is further metabolized by hydration to trans-CBZ-diol which is excreted by the urine [44].

The metabolism of CBZ during pregnancy may be unchanged, increased or decreased [45]. An increased CBZ-E/CBZ ratio during pregnancy has been demonstrated, and there appears to be an inhibition of the transformation of epoxide to the diol form [1]. This may have implications for the mechanism of teratogenicity.

Both CBZ and CBZ-E readily cross the placenta [1, 46], and the concentrations of free CBZ are equivalent in the fetal and the maternal circulations [1]. The cord plasma level of total CBZ is about 80% of the maternal blood level [46, 7]. The human fetal liver is able to metabolize CBZ into its epoxides [48]. A comparison between human fetal and adult livers has shown that the average epoxide hydrolase activity in the fetal liver is 25 – 30% that of the average adult enzyme activity [49]. As epoxides may be transferred directly from the mother to the fetus, a greater exposure of epoxides to the fetal cells is possible.

Combinations of AED

Pharmacokinetic interactions between CBZ and other AED are complex. CBZ may accelerate the metabolism of phenytoin, phenobarbital, primidone and valproic acid. Likewise, phenytoin, phenobarbital and primidone may increase the hepatic metabolism of CBZ [50].

Treatment of pregnant mothers with AED in combinations increases the risk of fetal malformations [27, 51, 52]. When 3 of more drugs are combined, the incidence rises dramatically. In two studies, the incidence of congenital malformations was $<4\%$ in 1-drug regimes and $>20\%$ in 4-drug regimes [27, 51]. Especially among infants exposed to the combination of CBZ, valproic acid, phenobarbital and, eventually, phenytoin, a very high percentage of anomalies is found [51]. It is possible that women in polytherapy differ from women in monotherapy regarding the severity of the epilepsy. However, the high rate of congenital malformations among infants exposed to the above-mentioned combination of drugs supports by hypothesis that combinations of AED possess teratogenic activity mediated through metabolic interactions [51].

Teratogenicity of CBZ

There are three sources of information of fetal effects of a specific agent: (a) experimental studies in animals, (b) case reports and (c) epidemiologic studies [11].

Since interactions between CBZ and other AED are common, it is necessary to look at offspring of mothers given CBZ monotherapy, in order to assess the teratogenic effects of CBZ itself.

Experimental Studies in Animals in Relation to CBZ

In 1976, Fritz et al. [53] made a comparative study of the teratogenicity of phenobarbital, diphenylhydantoin and CBZ in albino mice. The drugs were given between days 6 and 15 of gestation, i.e. in the period of organogenesis. CBZ was given orally in different doses. No significant change in the malformation rate was observed. The mean weight of treated animals was a little lower than in the control group, however, that difference was not statistically significant. The number of unossified phalangeal nuclei of the forelimb was slightly increased. The changes were considered to be due to a slight growth retardation.

Sullivan and McElhatton [54] made a comparative study of the teratogenicity of CBZ and 5 other AED. CD-1 mice were treated on days 6 – 16 of pregnancy with oral doses of 3, 9 and 16 times the therapeutic dose for humans. No significant difference in fetal weights compared to the control group was seen. The incidence of fetal defects was about 3.5 times higher than that in the control group.

Eluma et al. [55] investigated the teratogenic effect of dosage and time of administration of CBZ, sodium valproate and diphenylhydantoin on craniofacial development in CD-1 mice. Three different doses were given orally on gestation days 8 – 10, 11 – 13, 14 – 16 or day 8 – 16. A significant decrease in mean fetal weight was found, indicating a drug-induced, time-dependent and dose-related intra-uterine growth retardation. Compared with sodium valproate and diphenylhydantoin, CBZ had the least teratogenic and embryotoxic effects.

Paulson et al. [56] compared the effect of phenytoin and CBZ as a cause of cleft palates in CD-1 Swiss albino mice. The doses of CBZ included a very high dose (1,600 mg/kg) that was given orally from day 8 to 13 during gestation. Only a few cases of cleft palates were found, and the teratogenic effect of CBZ for full-length cleft palates was not statistically significant.

El-Sayed et al. [57] gave albino rats CBZ orally in therapeutic and double therapeutic doses on days 9 – 17 of pregnancy. CBZ in both doses produced a significant increase in the number of fetal deaths. In the lowest dose, CBZ decreased the length of the fetuses. Compared to phenytoin and ethosuximide, CBZ caused a lower incidence of skeletal and visceral malformations. Histopathological examination of the fetal brains showed congestion of meningeal blood vessels with lymphocytic infiltration. Haemorrhage within the pyramidal cell layer of the cerebrum, could be observed. Hydrocephalus was found in about 15% of the fetuses exposed to CBZ, but less frequently than in the fetus exposed to phenytoin and ethosuximide.

Vorhees et al. [58] investigated the teratogenicity of CBZ in Sprague-Dawley CD rats with 3 different oral doses of CBZ given on days 7 – 18 of gestation. The maternal serum CBZ concentration was much higher than therapeutic levels in humans. In all three dose groups, there was a dose-related reduction in fetal weight. Rats treated with CBZ in the highest dose had an increased number of skeletal and visceral abnormalities, whereas rats treated with CBZ in the lowest dose showed no significant abnormalities. The authors concluded that, in rats, CBZ is mildly teratogenic and embryocidal. Its largest embryotoxic effects are upon fetal body weight.

Another type of animal study was performed by Dow and Riopelle [59] on developing neurons in vitro. They examined the effects of 4 AED (among them CBZ) in a dose-dependent manner on dissociated cultures of embryonic chick dorsal root ganglia neurons. All 4 drugs inhibited process formation, but inhibition with phenobarbital and CBZ was less than with diphenylhydantoin and valproic acid. The data suggest a rank ordering of direct toxic effects of anticonvulsants on development neurons. But as the authors have stated, the in vitro system does not permit direct comparisons to be made between concentrations of anticonvulsants in the tissue culture medium and concentrations in vivo.

In conclusion, it seems that CBZ is slightly teratogenic in animals. Experimental studies in animals allow for tests of drug effects in well-controlled situations. However, the effects in animals may not be the same as in humans.

Case Stories in Relation to CBZ Monotherapy

Different malformations in the offspring of mothers in CBZ monotherapy have been described as anecdotal reports [13, 60–64]. Congenital rib anomalies [60], partial agenesis of the 7th and 12th cranial nerve nuclei [61], optic nerve hypoplasia [62] and spina bifida [63] have been reported. A physically and mentally retarded infant with dysmorphic features has been described [64].

Jones et al. [13], in the retrospective part of their paper, reported details on 4 children exposed to CBZ monotherapy; 1 child had pre-and postnatal growth deficiency, microcephaly, developmental delay, cardiac defect (tetralogy of Fallot), upslanting palpebral fissures, short nose with long philtrum and hypoplastic nails; another had postnatal growth deficiency, microcephaly and developmental delay; the 3rd child had prenatal growth deficiency and hypoplastic nails, and the 4th child had no defects. The authors claim that a pattern of malformations, the principal features of which are minor craniofacial defects and finger-nail hypoplasia, and of developmental delay, has been identified in the children.

Case reports can be very useful to alert the scientific forum to some particular aspects of a problem and to stimulate further studies, but obviously they are uncontrolled and may be biased. Epidemiologic studies are the only way to determine if an agent causes an increased risk of fetal damage in humans.

Epidemiologic Studies in Relation to CBZ Monotherapy

Different epidemiologic studies of the offspring of mothers taking AED have been performed. The major studies concerning CBZ-monotherapy are briefly discussed.

Bertollini et al. [26] have collected material from four parts of Europe. The material includes data on 577 infants whose mothers used AED in monotherapy in early pregnancy; 70 received CBZ monotherapy. The total rate of malformations was 3.5%, which is higher than that expected from the general population. However, the malformation rate for CBZ was the lowest observed in the study (1.4%). The reduction of fetal growth was greater for CBZ than for the other AED.

The long-term effects of ante-natal exposure to CBZ and phenobarbital on central nervous system development have been evaluated by van der Pol et al. [36]. 57 children aged 6–13 years, of epileptic mothers, were studied and compared to a matched control group. Four subgroups were distinguished in the study population according to specific ante-natal drug exposure: CBZ, CBZ + phenobarbital, phenobarbital and no drug exposure. No significant differences were found in the occurrence of (minor) neurologic dysfunction, neither between the control group and the study groups as a whole nor between the control group and the specific drug groups. Both minor and major physical anomalies were more frequent in children of epileptic mothers than in children of non-epileptic mothers. Lindhout et al. [51, 65] performed a prospective cohort study of pregnancies with maternal epilepsy from 1972–1979 [51] and 1980–1985 [65]. The last part of the study concerns 172 children, including 35 exposed to CBZ monotherapy. 5 infants had malformations: 1 spina bifida occulta, 1 spina bifida (this child was also exposed to the pill in the first trimester), 1 glandular hypospadias, 1 inguinal hernia and 1 cleft lip. The mothers of malformed infants tended to have higher drug levels in serum. The authors reported a lower frequency of malformations in the second period, where the use of polytherapy had decreased.

Wladimiroff et al. [66] studied the value of ultrasound in the early diagnosis of fetal structural defects following maternal anticonvulsant therapy in 162 pregnant women. After delivery, a careful search for congenital defects was made by a neonatologist. In any case of pregnancy termination as a result of lethal structural defects, a post-mortem examination was carried out. 45 women had CBZ as monotherapy, including 1 case where the pregnancy was terminated due to severe hydrocephaly. The total incidence of malformations was 3.6%, and this incidence was not related to a specific drug.

In a study from Finland [35, 67, 68] 139 epileptic women were followed during 151 pregnancies resulting in 153 offspring. In 21 pregnancies, the mothers used CBZ monotherapy, and malformations were found in 2 children [35]. Obstetric complications and interventions occurred among epileptic women as frequently as among the matched control group [67]. A comparison was made between 4 anticonvulsant regimes, no AED, and controls concerning head circumference, weight and length at birth. CBZ was found to be associated with smaller head circumferences [68]. At follow-up, when the children were 5.5 years old, 2 of the children exposed to CBZ alone were shorter than 2 standard deviations (SD) below the mean of controls, but they had normal head circumferences and normal intelligence. 1 child had a head smaller than −2 SD but normal height and intelligence [35]. 1 child in the study group had severe mental deficiency. She had infantile spasms during her 1st year of life, her growth and head circumference were normal, and except for mild distal phalangeal hypoplasia, she had no other anomalies [35].

In a prospective study, Jones et al. [13] investigated the outcomes of pregnancy in 72 women who contacted them early in pregnancy because they were concerned about the potential teratogenicity of CBZ. 48 children were examined, including 35 exposed to CBZ alone. No statistically significant excess of major malformations was observed among children exposed to CBZ compared to controls of non-epileptic mothers. Minor abnormalities were more common in the exposed children than in the controls. The authors suggest that CBZ exposure is associated with a pattern of minor malformations rather than 1 or more major malformations.

In Japan, data were collected prospectively from 1978 to 1984 on 172 infants born to epileptic mothers [52]. 141 patients treated with multiple AED had a rate of malformation of 15.6%, 31 patients in monotherapy had a rate of malformation of 6.5%, 10 patients were treated with CBZ alone, and in 1 offspring a malformation was seen (extensive naevus).

Effect of CBZ on Specific Factors in Neonatal Development and the Risk for Spina Bifida

Growth and Head Circumferences

In two studies head circumference, weight and length at birth were smaller in CBZ-exposed neonates than in infants exposed to AED other than CBZ [26, 46].

Jones et al. [13] found no significant difference in birth length and head circumference at birth between infants exposed to CBZ (mono- and polytherapy) and controls. However, birth weight was just significantly lower than in controls.

Hiilesmaa et al. [68] found that mean head circumference (standardized for gestational age and sex) of infants born to mothers given CBZ alone was 7 mm less than that of controls. This difference is claimed to be significant, but it is indeed small and may not be of clinical relevance. No remarkable differences were observed for weight and length. Most of these children were examined again at 5.5 years of age. Only 1 child exposed to CBZ monotherapy had a head smaller than -2 SD of the control mean; this child had normal height and intelligence [35].

In agreement with this, van der Pol et al. [36] found that children born to CBZ-treated mothers had head circumference above that of the controls. Weight and height distribution at follow-up did not differ from that of the controls. In this study children aged 6–13 years were examined.

In conclusion, it is uncertain, although possible, that CBZ may reduce intra-uterine growth. The effect is small and of uncertain clinical significance.

Mental Development

A few studies with neurobehavioural assessments have been performed in children exposed to CBZ monotherapy in utero.

Jones et al. [13] tested 25 children by the Bayley Scales of Infant Development, Stanford-Binet IV intelligence scale for children or the Wechsler Scale of Preschool and Primary Intelligence. They found that 5 children (20%) had developmental delays because they scored $\leqslant 1$ SD below the mean on the tests. However, it must be remembered that in a normally distributed population, 16% will fall below the limit of -1 SD. No control groups were used in the evaluations of the developmental delay. The result falls within the 95% confidence limits [69], and is probably not significant. Furthermore, the results are biased by the fact that only 25 of the total number of 35 children were examined. This means that the finding of Jones et al. [13] is not at all alarming.

Van der Pol et al. [36] tested 112 children aged 6–13 years, including 11 children who had been exposed to CBZ monotherapy. A standardized and age-specific neurologic examination was carried out with special emphasis on the presence of minor neurologic dysfunctions. Three short standardized Dutch tests for reading, spelling and arithmetic were applied. The parents and teachers completed an identical questionnaire on the child's behaviour. No significant differences were found in the occurrence of (minor) neurologic dysfunctions, neither between the control and the study group as a whole nor between the control and the specific drug groups. The results of the tests for reading, spelling and arithmetic were similar in the four groups, however, the phenobarbital group showed a surplus of poor performers. No differences between the control and the study groups were found in the children's behaviour questionnaire answered by the teachers and parents.

Hättig and Steinhausen [39] performed a prospective study in children of epileptic parents and matched controls. Behaviour was assessed three times during the 1st month of life. At the beginning of the 2nd year of life, the Home Inventory was used to record mother-child interaction in natural surroundings. Mental development was measured at 15 months of age using the Bayley Scale. At the age of 4–6 years, a variety of psychological tests was administered, and behavioural abnormalities were assessed by means of a structured interview with the mother. The functioning of infants exposed to AED was poorer than that of the controls during the 1st and 2nd weeks, but no differences were found during the 4th week of life. Polytherapy and valproic acid were related to impaired Bayley-test functioning, but were still within the normal range. The study included 4 children exposed to CBZ monotherapy, and their mental development index did not differ from that of the controls.

In the Finnish study, only 1 of 121 children had severe mental deficiency [35]. This child had been exposed to CBZ alone (maximal level 12 μmol/l) and had infantile spasms during her 1st year of life.

In sum, only few studies have dealt with mental development in children exposed to CBZ. These studies do not show a significant correlation between CBZ and developmental delay.

Minor Anomalies

Jones et al. [13] described a pattern of minor craniofacial defects and fingernail hypoplasia in infants exposed to CBZ. Epicanthal folds were the most frequent craniofacial defect and were found in 26% of the infants; other defects were less frequent. The number of infants whose mothers were treated with CBZ (alone or in combination) with 2 minor anomalies was not significantly higher than in the controls, but the number of infants with ⩾3 minor defects was significant [13].

In a study from the Netherlands, minor anomalies were more frequent in offspring of epileptic mothers than those of non-epileptic mothers. However, the children exposed to CBZ did not differ from non-exposed children born to epileptic mothers [36].

In a German study, minor anomalies were less frequent in the CBZ group compared to infants exposed to AED other than CBZ, and as frequent as in a matched-pair control group of unexposed neonates [46].

To sum up children of epileptic mothers have minor defects more often than children of non-epileptic mothers. Children exposed to CBZ are probably less often affected or affected in a lower degree compared to children exposed to other AED.

Major Malformations

Table 1 summarizes the epidemiologic studies which include the offspring of mothers in CBZ monotherapy [13, 16, 26, 35, 36, 46, 51, 52, 65–68, 70–75]. Major malformations are reported in 15 of 278 children. The malformations differ and include 3 cases of spina bifida (1 spina bifida occulta and 2 spina bifida aperta), 3 cases of cardiac defects (1 severe, 1 without haemodynamic consequences, 1 unknown), 3 cases of inguinal hernia, 3 cases of hypospadias, 1 cleft lip, 1 bilateral cleft lip and palate, 1 hydrocephaly, 1 hip dislocation and 1 extensive naevus. The results of these studies are not comparable, because the diagnosis of many congenital malformations varies with the observer. Furthermore, for some malformations, the reported incidence is dependent on the length of follow-up.

Spina Bifida

The association between valproic acid and spina bifida is well known [65, 76–79]. In a multinational study where data on infants were collected from 6 birth defect monitoring registries, a weak and non-significant associa-

Table 1. Studies of malformations in children of epileptic mothers treated with CBZ in monotherapy

Reference	Location	period	n[1]	CBZ monotherapy		
				n[2]	malformations	type of defect
Bertollini et al. [26]	France	1973–83	224	13	0	
	France	1976–84	50	3	0	
	Italy	1983–85	49	5	0	
	Sweden	1973–81	254	49	1	hypospadias
Starreveld-Zimmerman et al. [70]	Netherlands	1971–72	297	1	0	
van der Pol et al. [36]	Netherlands	1973–81	57	11	1	cardiac anomalies
Lindhout et al. [51]	Netherlands	1972–79	151	12	0	
Lindhout [65]	Netherlands	1980–85	172	35	5	spina bifida occulta, spina bifida, hypospadias, inguinal hernia, cleft lip
Wladimiroff et al. [66]	Netherlands	1982–87	164	45	2	hydrocephaly + bilateral cleft lip and palate + hypospadias, small muscular VSD
Meyer [71]	FRG	p: 1973	313	1	0	
Koch et al. [16]	FRG	1976–81	70	2	0	
Kuhnz et al. [46]	FRG	p: 1983	12	8	0	
Gaily et al. [35] Hiilesmaa et al. [67, 68]	Finland	1976–79	153	21	2	inguinal hernia, hip dislocation
Kelly et al. [72]	USA	1977–82	171	2	0	
Jones et al. [13]	USA	1979–89	48	35	3	meningomyelocele, multiple VSD, inguinal hernia
Barry and Danks [73]	Australia	1967–72	93	3	0	
Kaneko et al. [52]	Japan	1978–84	172	10	1	extensive naevus
Tanaka et al. [74]	Japan	p: 1991	82	18	0	
Bag et al. [75]	India	p: 1989	30	4	0	
			Sum	278	15	

VSD = Ventricular septal defect; p: (year) = published in (year).
1 Children of epileptic mothers being studied.
2 Children exposed to CBZ monotherapy.

tion between CBZ and spina bifida was seen [76].

Rosa [79] has analyzed data on 22 cohort studies and found that exposure to CBZ in utero without exposure to valproic acid carries a 1% risk of spina bifida [79]. However, he has quoted that 1 child with spina bifida found by Robert et al. [33] was exposed to

CBZ without valproic acid, but according to Robert et al. [33], this child was exposed to both CBZ and valproic acid. If corrected for this, the incidence is 0.8%. When calculating the risk, Rosa did not distinguish between exposure to CBZ alone or in combination with other AED except valproic acid. But he mentioned that 5 of the 10 cases of spina bifida occurred in infants of mothers in CBZ monotherapy during pregnancy [79].

In summary, exposure to CBZ in utero carries a small risk of spina bifida. This risk is greater than for most other AED, but certainly not as high as that for valproic acid.

Conclusion

Animal experiments have established that CBZ has minor teratogenic effects. Histopathological examination of fetal brains has shown hydrocephalus, congestion of meningeal blood vessels and haemorrhage within the pyramidal cell layer of the cerebrum. A direct toxic effect of CBZ on development neurons has been shown.

In humans, it is not possible to identify a specific pattern related to exposure to CBZ in utero. Like other AED, CBZ may be associated with different minor anomalies.

Exposure to CBZ in utero carries a small risk of spina bifida. This risk is probably greater than for most other AED, but not as high as for valproic acid.

No association between CBZ and brain dysfunction has been established, but only few studies have yet dealt with this possibility.

Monotherapy is less teratogenic than polytherapy, but no AED is absolutely safe. CBZ in monotherapy is to be regarded as a human teratogen, but with rather low teratogenic potential.

References

1 Yerby MS: Problems and management of pregnant woman with epilepsy. Epilepsia 1987;28(suppl 3):29–36.
2 Teramo K, Hiilesmaa VK: Pregnancy and fetal complications in epileptic pregnancies: Review of the literature; in Janz D, et al (eds): Epilepsy, Pregnancy and the Child. New York, Raven Press, 1982, pp 53–59.
3 Patterson RM: Seizure disorders in pregnancy. Med Clin North Am 1989;73:661–665.
4 Anonymous: Teratogenesis with carbamazepine. Lancet 1991;i:1316–1317.
5 Janz D, Fuchs U: Sind antiepileptische Medikamente während der Schwangerschaft schädlich? Dtsch Med Wochenschr 1964;89:241–243.
6 Anonymous: Carbamazepine update. Lancet 1989; ii:595–597.
7 Paulson GW, Paulson RB: Teratogenic effects of anticonvulsants. Arch Neurol 1981;38:140–143.
8 Friis ML: Antiepileptic drugs and teratogenesis. Acta Neurol Scand 1983;(suppl 94):39–43.
9 Saunders M: Epilepsy in women of childbearing age. BMJ 1989;299:581.
10 Niebyl JR, Blake DA, Freeman JM, Luff RD: Carbamazepine levels in pregnancy and lactation. Obstet Gynecol 1979;53:139–140.
11 Bossi L: Fetal effects of anticonvulsants; in Morselli PL, Pippenger CE, Penry JK (eds): Antiepileptic Drug Therapy in Pediatrics. New York, Raven Press, 1983, pp 37–64.
12 Robertson IG: Epilepsy in pregnancy. Clin Obstet Gynaecol 1986;13:365–384.
13 Jones KL, Lacro RV, Johnson KA, Adams J: Pattern of malformations in the children of women treated with carbamazepine during pregnancy. N Engl J Med 1989;320:1661–1666.
14 Leppig KA, Werler MM, Cann CI, Cook CA, Holmes LB: Predictive value of minor anomalies. I. Association with major malformations. J Pediatr 1987;110:531–537.
15 Andermann E, Dansky L, Andermann F, Loughnan PM, Gibbons J: Minor congenital malformations and dermatoglyphic alterations in the offspring of epileptic women: A clinical investigation of the teratogenic effects of antivulsant medication; in Janz D, et al (eds): Epilepsy, Pregnancy and the Child. New York, Raven Press, 1982, pp 235–249.

16 Koch S, Göpfert-Geyer I, Jäger-Roman E, et al: Antiepileptika während der Schwangerschaft. Dtsch Med Wochenschr 1983;108:250–257.
17 Janz D: On major malformations and minor anomalies in the offspring of parents with epilepsy: Review of the literature; in Janz D, et al (eds): Epilepsy, Pregnancy and the Child. New York, Raven Press, 1982, pp 211–222.
18 Speidel BD, Meadow SR: Maternal epilepsy and abnormalities of the fetus and newborn. Lancet 1972;ii:839–843.
19 Millar JHD, Nevin NC: Congenital malformations and anticonvulsant drugs. Lancet 1973;i:328.
20 Bjerkedal T, Bahna SL: The course and outcome of pregnancy in women with epilepsy. Acta Obstet Gynecol Scand 1973;52:245–248.
21 Fedrick J: Epilepsy and pregnancy: A report from the Oxford record linkage study. Br Med J 1973; ii:442–448.
22 Hill RM, Verniaud WM, Horning MG, McCulley LB, Morgan NR: Infants exposed in utero to antiepileptic drugs. Am J Dis Child 1974;127: 645–653.
23 Shapiro S, Slone D, Hartz SC, et al: Anticonvulsants and parental epilepsy in the development of birth defects. Lancet 1976;i:272–275.
24 Niswander JD, Wertelecki W: Congenital malformation among offspring of epileptic women. Lancet 1973;i:1062.
25 Kelly TE: Teratogenicity of anticonvulsant drugs. I. Review of the literature. Am J Med Genet 1984; 19:413–434.
26 Bertollini R, Källen B. Mastroiacovo P, Robert E: Anticonvulsant drugs in monotherapy. Effect on the fetus. Eur J Epidemiol 1987;3:164–171.
27 Nakane Y, Okuma T, Takahashi R, et al: Multi-institutional study on the teratogenicity and fetal toxicity of antiepileptic drugs: A report of a collaborative study group in Japan. Epilepsia 1980; 21:663–680.
28 Lowe CR: Congenital malformations among infants born to epileptic women. Lancet 1973;i: 9–10.
29 Annegers JF, Elveback LR, Hauser WA, Kurland LT: Do anticonvulsants have a teratogenic effect? Arch Neurol 1974;31:364–373.
30 Weber M, Schweitzer M, Mur JM, André M, Tridon P, Vert P: Pharmacologie pédiatrique. Epilepsie, médicaments antiépileptiques et grossesse. Arch Fr Pédiatr 1977;34:374–383.
31 Seino M, Miyakoshi M: Teratogenic risks of antiepileptic drugs in respect to the type of epilepsy. Folia Psychiatr Neurol Jpn 1979;33:379–385.
32 Dansky L, Andermann E, Andermann F: Major congenital malformations in the offspring of epileptic patients: Genetic and environmental risk factors; in Janz D, et al (eds): Epilepsy, Pregnancy and the Child. New York, Raven Press, 1982, pp 223–234.
33 Robert E, Löfkvist E, Mauguière F, Robert JM: Evaluation of drug therapy and teratogenic risk in Rhône-Alpes district population of pregnant epileptic women. Eur Neurol 1986;25: 436–443.
34 Rating D, Jäger-Roman E, Koch S, Göpfert-Geyer I, Helge H: Minor anomalies in the offspring of epileptic parents; in Janz D, et al (eds): Epilepsy, Pregnancy and the Child. New York, Raven Press, 1982, pp 283–288.
35 Gaily E, Granström ML, Hiilesmaa V, Bardy A: Minor anomalies in offspring of epileptic mothers. J Pediatr 1988;112:520–529.
36 van der Pol MC, Hadders-Algra M, Huisjes HJ, Touwen BCL: Antiepileptic medication in pregnancy: Late effects on the children's central nervous system development. Am J Obstet Gynecol 1991;164:121–128.
37 Majewski F, Raff W, Fischer P, Huenges R, Petruch F: Zur Teratogenität von Antikonvulsiva. Dtsch Med Wochenschr 1980;105:719–723.
38 Hill RM, Verniaud WM, Rettig GM, Tennyson LM, Craig JP: Relationship between antiepileptic drug exposure of the infant and developmental potential; in Janz D, et al (eds): Epilepsy, Pregnancy and the Child. New York, Raven Press, 1982, pp 409–417.
39 Hättig H, Steinhausen HC: Children of epileptic parents: A prospective developmental study; in Rauh H, Steinhausen HC (eds): Psychobiology and Early Development. Amsterdam, Elsevier, 1987, pp 155–169.
40 Steinhausen HC, Nestler V, Huth H: Psychopathology and mental functions in the offspring of alcoholic and epileptic mothers. J Am Acad Child Psychiatry 1982;21:268–273.
41 Granström ML: Development of the children of epileptic mothers: Preliminary results from the prospective Helsinki study; in Janz D, et al (eds): Epilepsy, Pregnancy and the Child. New York, Raven Press, 1982, pp 403–408.

42 Bertilsson L, Tomson T: Clinical pharmacokinetics and pharmacological effects of carbamazepine and carbamazepine-10,11-epoxide. Clin Pharmacokinet 1986;11:177 – 198.

43 Gillham RA, Williams N, Wiedmann K, Butler E, Larkin JG, Brodie MJ: Concentration-effect relationship with carbamazepine and its epoxide on psychomotor and cognitive function in epileptic patients. J Neurol Neurosurg Psychiatry 1988; 51:929 – 933.

44 Eichelbaum M, Tomson T, Tybring G, Bertilsson L: Carbamazepine metabolism in man. Induction and pharmacogenetic aspects. Clin Pharmacokinet 1985;10:80 – 90.

45 Bardy AH, Teramo K, Hiilesmaa VK: Apparent plasma clearances of phenytoin, phenobarbitone, primidone, and carbamazepine during pregnancy: Results of the prospective Helsinki study; in Jans D, et al (eds): Epilepsy, Pregnancy and the Child. New York, Raven Press, 1982, pp 141 – 145.

46 Kuhnz W, Jäger-Roman E, Rating D, et al: Carbamazepine and carbamazepine-10,11-epoxide during pregnancy and postnatal period in epileptic mothers and their nursed infants: Pharmacokinetics and clinical effects. Pediatr Pharmacol 1983;3:199 – 208.

47 Froescher W, Eichelbaum M, Niesen M, Altmann D, von Unruh GE: Antiepileptic therapy with carbamazepine and valproic acid during pregnancy and lactation period; in Dam M, Gram L, Penry JK (eds): Advances in Epileptology. 12th Epilepsy International Symposium. New York, Raven Press, 1981, pp 581 – 588.

48 Piafsky KM, Rane A: Formation of carbamazepine epoxide in human fetal liver. Drug Metab Dispos 1978;6:502 – 503.

49 Pacifici GM, Colizzi C, Giuliani L, Rane A: Cytosolic epoxide hydrolase in fetal and adult human liver. Arch Toxicol 1983;54:331 – 341.

50 Baciewicz AM: Carbamazepine drug interactions. Ther Drug Monit 1986;8:305 – 317.

51 Lindhout D, Höppener RJEA, Meinardi H: Teratogenicity of antiepileptic drug combinations with special emphasis on epoxidation (of carbamazepine): Epilepsia 1984;25:77 – 83.

52 Kaneko S, Otani K, Fukushima Y, et al: Teratogenicity of antiepileptic drugs: Analysis of possible risk factors. Epilepsia 1988;29:459 – 467.

53 Fritz H, Müller D, Hess R: Comparative study of the teratogenicity of phenobarbitone, diphenylhydantoin and carbamazepine in mice. Toxicology 1976;6:323 – 330.

54 Sullivan FM, McElhatton PR: A comparison of the teratogenic activity of the antiepileptic drugs carbamazepine, clonazepam, ethosuximide, phenobarbital, phenytoin, and primidone in mice. Toxicol Appl Pharmacol 1977;40:365 – 378.

55 Eluma FO, Sucheston ME, Hayes TG, Paulson RB: Teratogenic effects of dosage levels and time of administration of carbamazepine, sodium valproate, and diphenylhydantoin on craniofacial development in the CD-1 mouse fetus. J Craniofac Genet Dev Biol 1984;4:191 – 210.

56 Paulson RB, Paulson GW, Jreissaty S: Phenytoin and carbamazepine in production of cleft palates in mice. Comparison of teratogenic effects. Arch Neurol 1979;36:832 – 836.

57 El-Sayed MGA, Aly AE, Kadri M, Moustafa AM: Comparative study on the teratogenicity of some antiepileptics in the rat. East Afr Med J 1983; 60:407 – 415.

58 Vorhees CV, Acuff KD, Welsenburger WP, Minck DR: Teratogenicity of carbamazepine in rats. Teratology 1990;41:311 – 317.

59 Dow KE, Riopelle RJ: Differential effects of anticonvulsants on developing neurons in vitro. Neurotoxicology 1988;9:97 – 104.

60 Legido A, Toomey K, Goldsmith L: Congenital rib anomalies in a fetus exposed to carbamazepine. Clin Pediatr 1991;30:127 – 128.

61 Robertson IG, Donnai D, D'Souza S: Cranial nerve agenesis in a fetus exposed to carbamazepine. Dev Med Child Neurol 1983;25:540 – 541.

62 West J, Burke JP, Strachan I: Carbamazepine, epilepsy, and optic nerve hypoplasia. Br J Ophthalmol 1990;74:511.

63 Oakeshott P, Hunt GM: Carbamazepine and spina bifida. BMJ 1991;303:651.

64 Vestermark V, Vestermark S: Teratogenic effect of carbamazepine. Arch Dis Child 1991;66: 641 – 642.

65 Lindhout D: Teratogenesis in Maternal Epilepsy – New Aspects of Prevention; thesis Vrije Universiteit te Amsterdam, 1985, pp 81 – 105.

66 Vladimiroff JW, Stewart PA, Reuss A, van Swaay E, Lindhout D, Sachs ES: The role of ultrasound in the early diagnosis of fetal structural defects following maternal anticonvulsant therapy. Ultrasound Med Biol 1988;14:657 – 660.

67 Hiilesmaa VK, Bardy A, Teramo K: Obstetric out-

come in women with epilepsy. Am J Obstet Gynecol 1985;152:499–504.
68 Hiilesmaa VK, Teramo K, Granström ML, Bardy AH: Fetal head growth retardation associated with maternal antiepileptic drugs. Lancet 1981; ii:165–167.
69 Geigy Scientific Tables. Basel, Ciba-Geigy, 1982.
70 Starreveld-Zimmerman AAE, van der Kolk WJ, Meinardi H, Elshove J: Are anticonvulsants teratogenic? Lancet 1973;ii:48–49.
71 Meyer JG: The teratological effects of anticonvulsants and the effects on pregnancy and birth. Eur Neurol 1973;10:179–190.
72 Kelly TE, Edwards P, Rein M, Miller JQ, Dreifuss FE: Teratogenicity of anticonvulsant drugs. II. A prospective study. Am J Med Genet 1984;19: 435–443.
73 Barry JE, Danks DM: Anticonvulsants and congenital abnormalities. Lancet 1974;ii:48–49.
74 Tanaka H, Takeda A, Izumi M, Okada H, Ishikawa S: Effects of antiepileptic drugs on delivery and early childhood – Comparison among monotherapies of valproic acid, phenytoin, carbamazepine and phenobarbital (in Japanese). Rinsho Shinkeigaku 1991;31:266–269.
75 Bag S, Behari M, Ahuja GK, Karmarkar MG: Pregnancy and epilepsy. J Neurol 1989;236: 311–313.
76 Källen B, Robert E, Mastroiacovo P, Martinez-Frias ML, Castilla EE, Cocchi G: Anticonvulsant drugs and malformations. Is there a drug specificity? Eur J Epidemiol 1989;5:31–36.
77 Lindhout D, Meinardi H: Spina bifida and in-utero exposure to valproate. Lancet 1984;ii:396.
78 Lindhout D, Schmidt D: In-utero exposure to valproate and neural tube defects. Lancet 1986;i: 1392–1393.
79 Rosa FV; Spina bifida in infants of women treated with carbamazepine during pregnancy. N Engl J Med 1991;324;674–677.

Vibeke Vestermark, MD
Department of Gynecology and Obstetrics
Herlev University Hospital
Herlev Ringvej 75
DK–2730 Herlev (Denmark)

Dev Brain Dysfunct 1993;6:279 – 304

1019 – 5815/93/0065 – 0279$2.75/0

Prenatal Nicotine Exposure: Biochemical and Neuroendocrine Bases of Behavioral Dysfunction

Walter Lichtensteiger, Margret Schlumpf

Institute of Pharmacology, University of Zürich, Switzerland

Key Words. Fetus · Placenta · Tobacco · Nicotine · Receptors · Dopamine · Sexual dimorphism · Testosterone · Aromatase · Glucocorticoids

Abstract. Behavioral dysfunctions occur in children after cigarette smoking during pregnancy, and in experimental animals after prenatal exposure to components of tobacco smoke. Substances implicated in developmental alterations include carbon monoxide, cadmium, thiocyanate and, in particular, nicotine. Experimental model systems used to analyze the teratogenic action of this drug are discussed. Nicotine can affect fetal development indirectly, e.g. through effects on placental function, as well as directly. Nicotinic acetylcholine receptors appear in rat brain at late embryonic stages. Their regional ontogeny is described; it is influenced by prenatal nicotine exposure. Acute and long-term changes which can tentatively be related to typical behavioral dysfunctions are seen in the functional state of dopamine and norepinephrine systems. Drugs can also affect brain development by interfering with developmental actions of hormones. In the rat, prenatal nicotine exposure disturbs male sexual brain differentiation; it alters important steps in this process (testosterone secretion, brain aromatase activity). The drug also influences the developing adrenal axis. The delayed functional deficiencies thus appear as a result of the concerted action of various pathogenetic mechanisms.

Behavioral Dysfunctions

Tobacco (mainly cigarette) smoking in pregnancy has been associated with disturbances of human fetal motor behavior [1] and with behavioral dysfunctions in children, starting from the neonatal stage [2 – 13]. A recent report also describes neuropsychological deficits following passive smoking in pregnancy; the condition of these children was intermediary between children of nonsmokers and those of smokers [14]. The reports on effects of tobacco on brain development gave rise to considerable controversy, yet, the relationship appears to be well established by now.

Cigarette smoking exerts acute effects on fetal behavior. It reduces the incidence of fetal breathing movements both in humans and in experimental animals [15], and decreases fetal movements [1]. Neonates born to smokers have been found to exhibit altered auditory responsiveness and increased tremors [6, 7, 10], followed at 30 days by increased hypertonicity, heightened tremors and startles [11]. At later stages of development, the children show symptoms of minimal brain dysfunction (MBD, attention deficit disorder). Recent longitudinal studies with yearly examination demonstrate a continuity of dysfunctions in the same sample from the neonatal stage to 4 years of age [12, 13]. The development of verbal skills appears to be particularly sensitive [3, 9, 12, 13], but other aspects of cognitive function and memory are affected as well [3, 5, 8, 9, 12, 13]. The short attention span typical of MBD is emphasized by Naeye and Peters [9] hyperactivity has also been reported [4, 9]. The effects of smoking during pregnancy are dose-dependent. Significant behavioral alterations have been noted after more than 10 cigarettes/day [9] or 0.16 mg nicotine/day [12, 13]; in a number of scores, children exposed to lower doses ranged between those of nonsmokers and the higher exposed group.

The relative importance of different components of tobacco smoke (in particular nicotine and carbon monoxide) is difficult to assess in epidemiological investigations, however, animal studies have clearly identified nicotine as being a behavioral teratogen [16–26]. Prenatal nicotine exposure was followed by juvenile hyperactivity (rats), reduced exploratory activity (open field, rats, novel alley, guinea pigs), and deficits in learning behavior (rats and guinea pigs), and deficits in learning behavior (rats and guinea pigs), i.e. by behavioral alterations which in part are reminiscent of MBD symptoms. A reduction of open field activity has also been observed in offspring of rats exposed to tobacco smoke during pregnancy [27].

In some studies, male rat offspring were preferentially affected [21, 22, 25]. In children born to smoking mothers, male sex has been correlated with more pronounced reduction of fetal growth [28], hyperactivity [9], and greater misbehavior [5], but others failed to find sex differences [12, 13]. In rats, nicotine has further been found to interfere with the development of sexually dimorphic behavior [23, 26]. The possible role of interactions with neuroendocrine ontogeny is discussed in section Interactions with Neuroendocrine Brain Organization: Gonadal and Adrenal Axes.

Active Components of Tobacco Smoke

Tobacco smoke contains a number of potentially active compounds, in particular nicotine, carbon monoxide, thiocyanate, cadmium, and polycyclic aromatic hydrocarbons. The latter probably play a role in the transplacental carcinogenesis (especially leukemias) reported in clinical studies; this aspect will not be discussed here.

Carbon Monoxide

Fetal hypoxia is one of the possible etiological factors for developmental disturbances in children of cigarette smoking mothers; it can be caused by carbon monoxide as well as by effects of nicotine on blood circulation. Carbon monoxide has been considered as a major factor in adverse effects of cigarette smoking on the fetus; the condition of the fetus is particularly unfavorable because of the shift in the oxygen dissociation curve of fetal hemoglobin [16, 17, 29]. Under experimental conditions, carbon monoxide exposure during pregnancy was found to cause (pre- and postnatal) growth retardation [30–32]. However, the relative importance of carbon monoxide for human pregnancies remains uncertain. When neonates were matched according to carboxyhemoglobin levels in venous cord blood, children born to smoking mothers were still growth-retarded in comparison with children from nonsmoking mothers [33]. Fetal and maternal circulation was affected only by smoking tobacco cigarettes, but not by non tobacco cigarettes. Since both types of cigarettes increased maternal plasma carboxyhemoglobin concentrations, carbon monoxide appears to be of minor importance also with regard to changes in circulation [34].

Nicotine

Nicotine readily crosses the placental barrier; its levels in plasma of fetal animals [15, 35] and in human cord serum [36] were found to be comparable to, or higher than, those of the maternal blood. The drug may interfere with the development of the fetus in a number of different ways, i.e. by actions on the maternal organism, on the placenta, as well as on the fetus.

Actions of Nicotine on Placental and Fetal Circulation

Cigarette smoking or nicotine infusion increase vascular resistance and reduce intervillous blood flow of the placenta with both acute and chronic administration [37–41]. The chronic exposure can lead to degenerative changes in placental blood vessels [42, 43]. In a recent investigation, Burton and coworkers [44] confirmed the occurrence of pathological changes in the placenta of smokers. In particular, they noted a reduction of the volume fraction of fetal capillary lumina without change of the vascularity of the terminal villi, indicating a reduction of capillary size without change in capillary proliferation, and a thickening of the villous membrane. In principle, both acute and chronic changes in blood flow could impair the supply of oxygen and nutrients. However, the reduction of the diffusion capacity calculated from the data of Burton et al. [44] is relatively small, i.e. 10%; these authors felt that the placentofetal system should be capable of compensating a functional impairment of this magnitude. In this contex, it should be noted that chronic hypoxia has been found to induce opposite changes, i.e. a reduction of villous membrane thickness [45, 46]. Newborns from smokers and nonsmokers were found not to differ with respect to oxygen saturation of their blood, while certain central nervous depressants increased the number of desaturation episodes [47]. During the acute smoking phase, human fetal aortic blood flow was found to be increased in two recent investigations [34, 48]. Two earlier studies failed to detect a change in flow [49, 50]. This might provide some degree of compensation for the impaired uterine blood flow [34]. Fetal hypoxia has been described in sheep [15] and rhesus monkeys [51] following acute nicotine injection. However, in the sheep fetus, heart rate decreased and blood pressure rose, while human fetal heart rate increased in the presence of reduced peripheral resistance [34]. Hence, the relative significance of mechanisms leading to hypoxia remains uncertain.

The acute effect of nicotine may involve release of maternal catecholamines [40, 52], though an elevation of maternal catecholamine blood levels is not consistently observed [34]. Another pathogenic mechanism of potential importance is the interaction of cigarette smoking with eicosanoid synthesis pathways in placental blood vessels. Smoking is known to change the relation between prostacyclin and thromboxane A_2 in the adult cardiovascular system [53]. Umbilical arteries from smokers produce less prostacyclin [54]; the deficiency was inversely related to cord blood nicotine levels [55]. In both, smokers and nonsmokers, nicotine inhibits in vitro prostacyclin synthesis in umbilical arteries [56] and in endothelial cell cultures of umbilical veins [57], probably by an action on the cyclo-oxygenase step [58]. Nicotine has further been found to interfere with the synthesis of other eicosanoids such as thromboxane, prostaglandins and leukotrienes; however, the data so far are partially conflicting and appear to depend upon tissue and experimental conditions [59–63]. The diminished capacity of placental vessels for prostacyclin formation can be expected to disturb blood flow regulation by increasing the tendency to vasoconstriction [64, 65]; in particular, the capacity for vasodilation in asphyxia could be reduced.

Cadmium levels are elevated in placentas of smokers [66, 67]. This compound may contribute to the impairment of placental function, as placentas of rats fed with cadmium exhibited a thickening of the trophoblastic lining separating maternal from fetal circulation that was comparable to the condition seen in placentas of smokers [67]. Whole blood cadmium of smoking women was significantly correlated with decreased birthweight of their offspring [68].

Thiocyanate, derived from cyanide in tobacco smoke, has also been discussed as a factor possibly affecting fetal growth [69]; its significance remains uncertain for the present time.

Cigarette smoking also affects *placental metabolism*, in particular cholinergic mechanisms [70], amino acid transport [71], certain aspects of placental steroid metabolism [72], and metabolism of xenobiotics [73, 74], the latter obviously being due to the action of polycyclic aromatic hydrocarbons.

It appears from these various observations that deficits in oxygen supply and nutrition should be taken into account as possible pathogenetic factors in smoking-induced developmental disorders. Yet, their relative importance remains difficult to assess; it seems questionable whether effects of cigarette smoking on brain development could be explained solely on the basis of a 'hypoxic syndrome'. It is certainly necessary to search for additional *direct teratogenic* effects of tobacco components such as nicotine.

Actions of Nicotine and Experimental Models

The perception of tobacco smoke probably takes on a different significance in human smokers and laboratory animals; it can be expected to introduce a number of stressful influences that are difficult to control. Therefore, it seems preferable to investigate effects of individual components such as nicotine. Ideally, such a treatment should mimic the smoking pattern – puffs with short-lasting peaks of plasma nicotine against the background of a baseline nicotine level rising slowly throughout the waking period. Because of the short half-life of nicotine, an appropriate pattern is difficult to achieve with injections. A small number of daily injections (e.g. 2) requires comparatively high individual doses leading to elevated plasma peaks prone to cause fetal hypoxia [75]; more frequent injections would cause considerable handling stress to the pregnant dam. Therefore, a continuous administration of the drug by osmotic minipump (or, in some cases, by drinking water) has been chosen in most of the recent investigations [23, 75, 76].

If one intends to look for direct teratogenic

effects of nicotine on the fetus, the continuous application of low doses by osmotic minipump would indeed seem to represent the preferable approach because it avoids high plasma peaks which would more readily cause circulatory changes possibly resulting in hypoxia [15, 75]. Behavioral alterations have been observed after prenatal treatment of rats with the osmotic minipump [24, 25] or application of the drug via the drinking water [19, 21]. Hence, the repetitive induction of hypoxic states does not seem to be necessary for the production of behavioral dysfunctions.

A majority of behavioral and biochemical studies to be reviewed below are based on a daily dose of 6 mg/kg of nicotine (0.25 mg/kg/h). In pregnant rats, this dose yields nicotine plasma levels between 80 and 120 ng/ml [76, 77], i.e., approximately 3 – 5 times the baseline plasma level of heavy smokers [78 – 80]. This dose level is well tolerated by the pregnant dams; effects on growth of the offspring were absent [81] or marginal [23, 75] in the presence of signs of impaired brain development. More recently, comparable or, with some parameters, identical biochemical findings have been obtained with a daily dose of 1.5 – 2 mg/kg [0.0625 – 0.083 mg/kg/h; 77, 82, 83]. Since doses applied by osmotic minipump and nicotine plasma levels have been found to exhibit an approximately linear relationship [76], the lower doses would be expected to yield plasma levels at around 35 ng/ml.

Developmental Effects on Target Systems in the CNS

This review will focus on direct actions on the fetal brain thought to be mediated by nicotinic cholinergic receptors on one hand, and on effects on developing neuroendocrine systems on the other hand. These neurochemical and neuroendocrine alterations provide some insight into mechanisms that may be responsible for the delayed behavioral dysfunctions. However, it should be pointed out that the site of action of nicotine need not be restricted to the nicotinic acetylcholine receptor; for example, actions on eicosanoid synthesis of the type described above might also occur in the developing brain. Additional enzymatic effects of nicotine have become known, such as an inhibition of human fetal adrenal 11β-hydroxylase [84].

General Developmental Pattern of Nicotinic Acetylcholine Receptors and Ontogeny of Cortical Receptor Sites

A prerequisite for specific actions of nicotine on brain structures is the presence of nicotinic acetylcholine receptors (nAChR). Their early ontogeny has been studied with [^{3}H]nicotine which is an appropriate ligand for central nAChR sites [85 – 87], but does not distinguish between possible subtypes [88]. A different set of binding sites is labelled by α-bungarotoxin in the central nervous system [88, 89]; they do not overlap with the majority of central nicotinic acetylcholine binding sites [90] and show a different postnatal development [91].

A few biochemical studies have signalled the presence of nicotinic binding sites in fetal brain from late gestation (gestational day, GD, 16 and following days), but their early regional development remained unknown [92 – 94]. Using in vitro autoradiography, high affinity binding sites for [^{3}H]nicotine become detectable in rat spinal cord and caudal medulla oblongata at the end of the embryonic period, i.e. at GD 12 (table 1). (GD 1 = 24 h after mating period) [95 – 97]. By GD 14, receptor sites are observed throughout

Table 1. Regional ontogeny of high-affinity [^{3}H]nicotine binding sites in rat brain

	GD								PN			2.5 months
	12	13	14	15	16	18	20	22	6	14	27	
										III/IV	III/IV	III/IV
Telencephalon				VTE	SEP	CPU	SPL	SPL	SPL	SPL		
				RET			ENP					
Diencephalon			HYP	HAB	THA		POA					
					(DLG)		BST					
Mesencephalon		VTG	QPL	SNC	DTG		RUB					
		(SNC)										
Metencephalon		PONS		CEBE			CGR					
							DTG					
							PON					
Myelencephalon	MED						IOL	XII				
	OBL								COC			
Spinal cord	SPC											

Areas are mentioned when binding sites are first detected by in vitro autoradiography. BST = Bed nucleus of stria terminalis; CEBE = cerebellum; CGR = central gray (pons); COC = cochlear nucleus; CPU = caudate putamen; DLG = dorsolateral geniculate nucleus; DTG = dorsal tegmentum; ENP = endopiriform nucleus; HAB = medial habenula; HYP = hypothalamus; IOL = inferior olivary nucleus; MED OBL = medulla oblongata; POA = preoptic area; PON = pontine nuclei; QPL = quadrigeminal plate; RET = retina; RUB = nucleus ruber; SEP = septum; SNC = substantia nigra zona compacta; SPC = spinal cord; SPL = subplate layer of neocortex; THA = thalamus; VST = ventral striatum; VTE = ventral telencephalon; VTG = ventral tegmentum; III/IV = neocortex layers III and IV; XII = hypoglossal nucleus. Data from Naeff et al. [97].

lower brainstem, mesencephalon and parts of diencephalon, with increased densities in ventral locations. In the cerebellar anlage, nAChR appear by GD 15, in caudate-putamen by GD 18; the first neocortical receptor sites are seen in the subplate layer by GD 20. During the transition from late gestational to early postnatal stages, we observed a decrease of the density of [^{3}H]nicotine binding sites in many brainstem regions (with the notable exception of thalamus) and increases in forebrain, in particular in neocortex [97]. In an investigation on postnatal mouse brain, a comparable drop of the number of [^{3}H]nicotine binding sites was noted in hindbrain and cerebellum, and to lesser extent in midbrain and hypothalamus, during the first 3 weeks of life [91]. These authors found an increase in the number of receptor sites only in striatum, while the density in cortex remained constant. However, our autoradiographic data in the rat revealed that the development of neocortical binding sites is complex and differs between layers; it is discussed in more detail below. In some areas such as substantia nigra and thalamus, the postnatal development of nicotinic binding sites is not continuous but reaches a peak in the 2nd week of life [116]. What may be learned from these regional analyses is the fact that the distribution of both, regions expressing nicotinic binding sites as well as areas with highest densities of binding sites change markedly during ontogeny. The effect of nicotine on individual brain structures would thus be expected to change in relation to the ontogenetic stage.

Muscarinic cholinergic receptor sites likewise appear in the central nervous system at an early developmental stage, i.e. in spinal cord by GD 13, and develop according to a general caudorostral gradient. However, their regional developmental patterns differ from that of nicotinic cholinergic receptors [95, 96, 98].

The appearance of both nicotinic and muscarinic binding sites seems to be related to the stage of maturation of individual brain structures. They are detected only in zones of differentiated cells and are absent in matrix layers. Some relation to the development of cholinergic fiber systems is evident in neocortex (see below), while the paucity of data does not yet allow for a detailed comparison of neuron and receptor development at brainstem levels. Both receptor classes are also found in human fetal brain [99, 100].

The relation between the appearance of [^{3}H]nicotine binding sites and differentiation processes is most evident in neocortex. As described above, nicotinic receptors are detected first in the subplate (table 1) [95, 97]. Subplate and marginal zone represent the innermost and outermost layers, respectively, of the developing neocortex, beneath and above the cortical plate out of which layers II – VI will be formed. These two layers contain the earliest differentiated neurons [101 – 103] and are the sites of early synapse formation [104, 105]. The subplate zone is a zone where projections from thalamus [103] as well as ascending nonspecific projections such as the catecholamine systems first terminate [106].

Nicotinic binding sites appear in this location shortly after the arrival of fibers ascending from the cholinergic basal forebrain nuclei [107]. The position of receptor sites corresponds to that of a dense layer of choline acetyltransferase-positive nerve fibers [95]. It seems probable that these cholinergic projections form transient functional synapses with subplate neurons in analogy to other projection systems [108]. A role of this input for cortical development is suggested by disturbances in the cytoarchitectonic pattern after neonatal lesions of basal forebrain cholinergic neurons [109]. Nicotinic receptors would seem to play an important role in this process, as they are clearly accumulated in the subplate in contrast to muscarinic binding sites which show a diffuse distribution throughout the different neocortical layers at the same developmental stage [98]. Following the outgrowth of basal forebrain projections into the cortical plate [107], a band of elevated nicotinic receptor density is formed at the level of layers III/IV, i.e. in the adult location, during the 2nd postnatal week. This phase is accompanied by signs of high metabolic activity of cholinergic nucleus basalis neurons such as a maximum of perikaryon diameter [107, 110] and, in cortex, a peak of the ratio between synaptosomal choline uptake and choline acetyltransferase (ChAT) activity [111]. In parallel with the involution of the subplate layer, the deeply situated band of high nicotinic receptor density vanishes after the 2nd week [97].

Effect of Prenatal Nicotine Exposure on Nicotinic Receptor Sites

After chronic exposure to nicotine during most of the pregnancy or during its second half, the number of [^{3}H]nicotine binding sites is markedly increased in late fetal and early postnatal brain, with the exception of the late developing cerebellum [112 – 114]. As shown

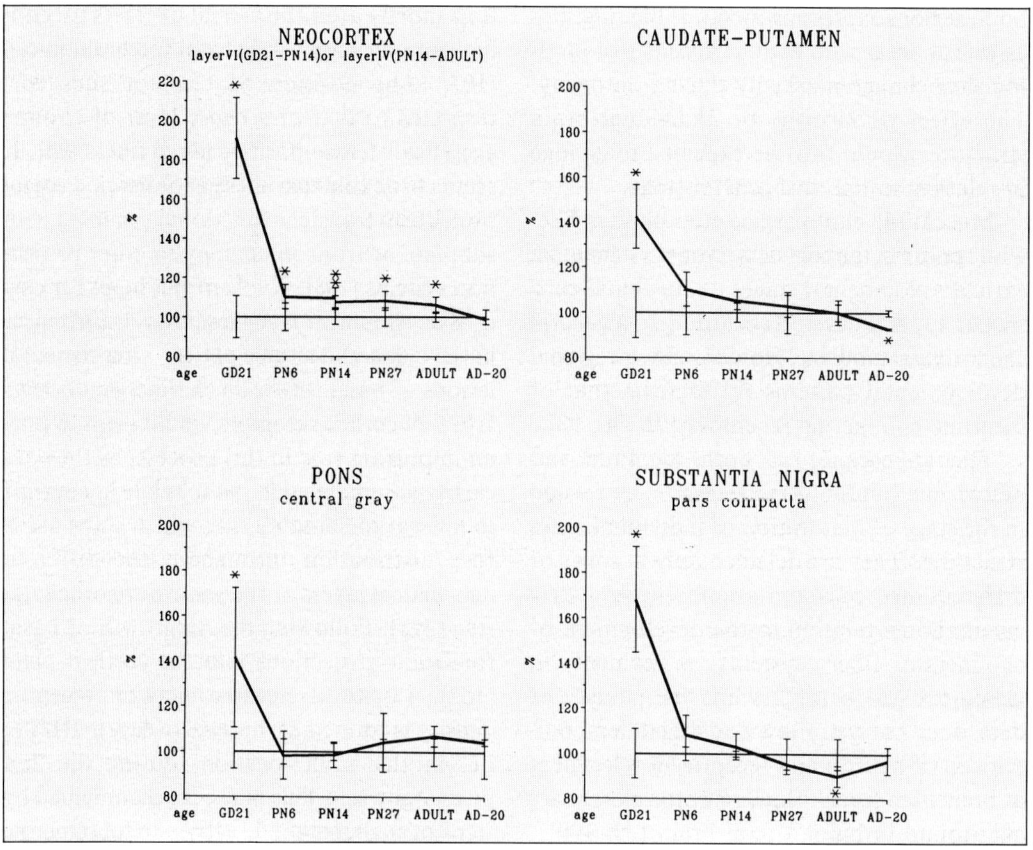

Fig. 1. Density of [3H]nicotine binding sites in several brain areas of male Long Evans rat fetuses and offspring following administration of nicotine bitartrate by osmotic minipump to time-pregnant dams (6 mg/kg/day; GD 12 to GD 19). During nicotine exposure, the density of receptor sites increases markedly in all brain regions. The subsequent nicotine-free postnatal period shows a general return of receptor densities towards control levels, though small, significant differences from controls remain in certain areas until adulthood. Neocortical data represent the subplate layer between GD 21 and PN 14, and layers III/IV between PN 14 and 20 months. Quantitative autoradiographic values were first converted to fmol bound ligand/mg protein and then expressed as percentage of controls born to dams implanted with osmotic minipumps filled with vehicle (mean + SD, from 4 – 8 pups/stage) *p < 0.05. ADULT = 2.5 months; AD 20 = 20 months. Data from Naeff-Odermatt [116; compare ref. No 115].

by quantitative autoradiography, the response is quite uniform in different brain areas (fig. 1) [115, 116]. This type of change resembles the increase in receptor number seen in adult animals after chronic nicotine treatment [117, 118], which suggests that in this case, the mechanism of receptor regulation might be similar in fetal and adult brain. However, the possibility that additional mechanisms specific of the developing brain might come into play has not been ruled out. No data are so far available on possible sex differences.

According to biochemical investigations, the alterations in the number of central nicotinic binding sites induced by prenatal nicotine exposure in midbrain and brainstem, cerebral cortex and cerebellum of rat offspring is normalized after a few weeks, before puberty [114]. However, a quantitative autoradiographic analysis demonstrates small but significant changes in nicotinic receptor density at even later stages (fig. 1) [115, 116]. In particular, binding site density remains above control levels in neocortex until the young adult stage (2.5 months), to become normalized at 20 months. The receptor population affected at these later stages is located in cortical layers III/IV and hence is different from the population (located in the subplate) which was increased during perinatal life. As no nicotinic receptors are expressed in layers III/IV during the period of drug exposure, the developmental signal leading to the delayed effect must be an indirect one. It has been argued that fiber systems innervating the subplate might influence developing neurons migrating through this zone on their way to their final destination in the cortical plate [103]. Nicotine might affect certain migrating neurons either directly or by effects on cholinergic neurons projecting to the subplate. Some indication for a disturbed function of these neurons can be seen in the reduced choline uptake/ChAT ratio of cerebral cortex during the first 2 postnatal weeks [111]. Of interest from a functional point of view are also two modifications in the nigrostriatal system (fig. 1). i.e. small but significant reductions in receptor density in substantia nigra at 2.5 months and in caudate-putamen at 20 months (compare section on catecholamine systems).

It should be noted that this discussion is based on data obtained with administration of nicotine by osmotic minipumps. If nicotine is administered to the pregnant dam by daily injections, different patterns of early postnatal alterations are observed [114]; analogous differences between treatments are also seen in the case of changes in catecholamine systems (see below).

Effect on Catecholamine Systems of the Fetal Brain: Possible Relationship to Behavioral Symptoms

The interaction of nicotine with fetal target neurons is well documented for central catecholamine systems. These systems may serve as an example for possible relationships between neurochemical and functional changes, in particular since they are known to be involved in certain functions disturbed by prenatal nicotine exposure, e.g. attention or control of motor behavior. In the rat, nicotinic receptor sites overlap with lower brainstem areas occupied by catecholamine neurons [119] from GD 14; the relationship is most clear-cut in the midbrain (GD 15) where high densities of nicotinic binding sites occur in the area of dopamine neurons [95].

Acute Actions on Fetal Catecholamine Systems. Information on acute effects of nicotine on neurotransmitter systems of the fetal brain so far is available only for catecholamine and serotonin systems; therefore, the acute effect will be discussed in this context. Nigrostriatal dopamine (DA) neurons [120, 121] and norepinephrine (NE) neurons of locus ceruleus [122] have been shown to receive a direct nicotinic input in adulthood. Single injections of nicotine to pregnant Long Evans rats (GD 21) elicited, within 30 min, a marked increase of DA and of its metabolites DOPAC and HVA in fetal forebrain of both sexes. A concomitant activation of NE systems is indicated by a significant rise of the

Table 2. Effect of chronic prenatal nicotine exposure on central catecholamine systems of male (M) and female (F) rat offspring

Author	Year	Treatment period	Brain region	Fetus gestational day GD 18
Lichtensteiger et al.	1988	GD 12–19	Forebrain	M: NE =, t.o. ↑ F: NE =, t.o. ↑
Ribary and Lichtensteiger	1989			M: DA =, t.o. ↑ F: DA =, t.o. =
Schlumpf et al.	1988	GD 12–19		
Fung and Lau	1989	GD 1–23	Striatum	
Fung	1988	GD 1–23		
Navarro et al.	1988	GD 4–20	Cortex	
Navarro et al.	1990	GD 4–20	Cortex	
Peters	1984	GD 1–23	Cortex	

DA, NE, concentrations, turnover (t.o.), receptor number and motor activity are shown.

Treatment: Alzet osmotic minipump execept for Peters [136] (nicotine in drinking water). Dose: 6 mg/kg/day except for Fung and Lau [83] (1.5 mg/kg/day).

Turnover analysis: Lichtensteiger et al. [95], Ribary and Lichtensteiger [81] and Fung and Lau [83]. Metabolite/catecholamine ratio (MOPEG/NE, DOPAC/DA, HVA/DA). Navarro et al. [125].

concentration ratio of the NE metabolite MOPEG to NE in males of this strain [81]. In fetuses of another rat strain (Sprague-Dawley), absolute levels of MOPEG were elevated in both sexes [123].

Chronic Effects. Prolonged prenatal exposure to nicotine initiates complex biochemical alterations in central catecholamine systems beyond the period of drug exposure; subtle alterations are detectable until adulthood [81]. The pattern of changes depends on developmental stage, brain region, and sex

Immature to juvenile			Adult 2.5 months
PN 1–2	PN 14/15	PN 45	
	M: NE ↑, t.o. ↓ F: NE =, t.o. ↓		M: NE =, t.o. ↓ F: NE, t.o. =
	M: DA ↑, t.o. ↓ F: DA ↑, t.o. =		M: DA =, t.o. ↓ F: DA, t.o. ↓
	Motor activity M ↑, F =		
	M: DA =, t.o. = F: DA =, t.o. = Dopamine D2 receptors: M ↓, F =		
	Motor activity: M ↑, F ↑		
M+F combined: NE ↓, t.o. ↓ DA ↓, t.o. ↓	M+F combined: NE =, t.o. = DA ↓, t.o. ↓	M+F combined: NE ↓, t.o. ↓ DA ↓, t.o. ↓	
NE receptors M+F combined: α_1 ↑, α_2, β =	NE receptors M+F combined: α_1 =, α_2, β =	NE receptors M+F combined: α_1 ↑ α_2, β =	
	M: NE ↑ F: NE = (data from PN 8)		M: NE = F: NE = NE receptors: β M ↑, F =, α_1 M =, F =, α_2 M ↑, F=

Reduction of catecholamine concentration 3 h after syntesis inhibition by α-methyltyrosine.

Receptor sites: Saturation experiment [B_{max}; 83] or determination at one concentration of labelled ligand [136, 143].

(table 2). Prenatal application of nicotine by daily subcutaneous injection or administration by (subcutaneously implanted) osmotic minipump differ in their delayed effects on catecholamine systems [124, 125]. Since the injection procedure introduces a number of variables that are difficult to control (see above), the following discussion will concentrate on data obtained with osmotic minipumps and will be limited to telencephalic areas where catecholamine turnover essentially reflects processes in nerve terminals.

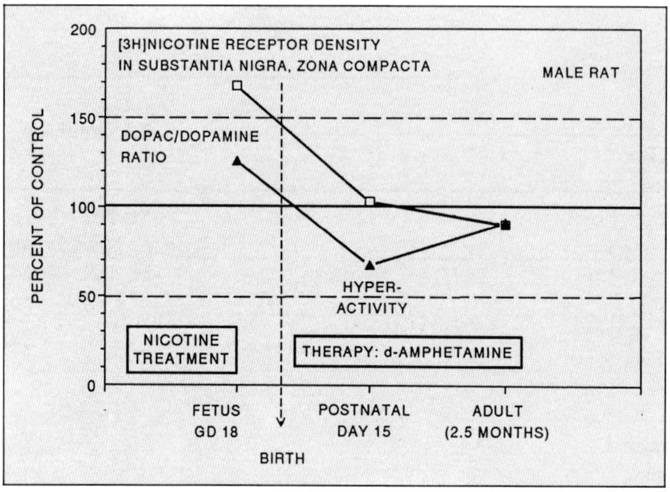

Fig. 2. Synopsis of neurochemical changes in the mesencephalic dopamine system and behavioral dysfunctions induced by prenatal nicotine exposure of the male rat. The fetal stage at the end of nicotine exposure is characterized by a marked increase in the density of [^{3}H]nicotine binding sites in zona compacta of substantia nigra in parallel with a rise in the forebrain DOPAC/DA ratio indicating an enhanced DA turnover. Following nicotine exposure, the DOPAC/DA ratio is reduced to below control levels at 15 and remains reduced until adulthood [81]. Nicotinic receptor density returns to control level at PN 15 and becomes slightly but significantly subnormal in young adult offspring [116]. Male offspring exposed to the same treatment are hyperactive at PN 15 [25]. The hyperactivity of prenatally nicotine-exposed rats is reduced by treatment with *d*-amphetamine [24].

In the fetus, the chronic condition is characterized by an increased turnover of NE in both sexes. In the male fetus, DOPAC was increased by 40%. In the presence of normalized DA levels, this results in an increase of the DOPAC/DA ratio, indicating enhanced DA turnover (table 2, fig. 2). In contrast, DA and its metabolites were at control levels in females [81]. This suggests the existence of a sex difference in the relative sensitivity of the developing DA system to nicotine already at the fetal stage. In the normal rat fetus, subtle sex differences have been detected in mesencephalic DA nerve cells before the classical time of onset of the period of sexual brain differentiation, in vitro at GD 14 and in vivo at GD 17 [126–128]; such differences could influence long-term effects of the drug.

With the transition to postnatal life and the drug-free state, forebrain NE turnover of both sexes is reversed to values below control level; in males, the alteration persists until adulthood [81] (table 2). This reduction of NE turnover was also seen during part of postnatal life in a combined analysis of cortex tissue from male and female pups [125]. It is accompanied by corresponding increases in the density of postsynaptic receptor sites, i.e., α_1-adrenergic binding sites in immature rats [129], and β-adrenergic receptors in adult males [130]. The basis of these persistent alterations remains unknown. The increased cortical α_2-receptor density in adult males [130] points to a possible involvement of presynaptic regulatory processes. It should be noted that the pattern of changes differs between brain regions [125]. A surprising finding is the increased NE turnover in cerebellum at postnatal days (PN) 35–45 (later stages were not studied), since these projections also originate in the locus ceruleus. This might again indicate some local influence on amine release.

With respect to behavioral dysfunctions reported in children, the condition of the immature rat offspring at about 2 weeks of life is of particular interest (table 2, fig. 2). Behavioral dysfunctions after prenatal nicotine exposure and attention deficit disorder (MBD) share a number of common features; the latter has been linked with postnatal dysfunction of dopamine systems [131]. At the 2-week stage, hyperactivity was observed in prenatally nicotine-exposed rats, either in both sexes [24] or selectively in males [25]. As with children suffering from MBD, the hyperactivity of prenatally nicotine-exposed rats was diminished by administration of *d*-amphetamine [24]. Control pups were stimulated. Biochemical studies of this developmental stage so far are not in complete agreement, but indicate an involvement of DA systems. Under conditions resulting in male hyperactivity, DA turnover was reduced in the forebrain of males [with some indication for a similar tendency in females; 81]; an analogous turnover reduction was found in cerebral cortex of a combined sample of male and female specimens [125]. In contrast, no significant alteration of DA turnover (DOPAC and DA values or their ratio) was detected in striatum [83], but in that study, a change in D2 receptor binding – again confined to males – and the efficiency of *d*-amphetamine point to an involvement of DA (or catecholamine) systems. It seems possible that nicotine-induced developmental changes were more pronounced in the mesolimbic DA system which was contained in the 'forebrain' and 'cortex' tissue pieces, since a relatively stronger effect of nicotine on that DA system has been reported for adulthood [132]. The treatment periods of the various investigations all cover the phase of development of catecholamine neurons in lower brainstem and mesencephalon [119]; in the study on striatum, a lower dose of nicotine was used (table 2).

The indications for a higher sensitivity of developing DA systems of the male are interesting in the light of human data on MBD which is more frequent in boys [133, 134]. As mentioned above, some behavioral dysfunctions also appear to be more easily induced by prenatal nicotine exposure in the male.

It seems noteworthy that (in both sexes), a small but significant alteration of DA turnover was found to persist until adulthood [81, 95], since substantia nigra and caudate-putamen are among the areas exhibiting late changes in nicotinic receptor density (at 2.5 and 20 months of age, respectively, fig. 1) [115, 116].

Changes in Other Neurotransmitter Systems

This discussion has been centered on cholinergic and adrenergic transmitter systems because the available information is comparatively detailed and reveals some relation between neurochemical changes and behavioral symptoms. Central serotonergic systems of the rat fetus were analyzed in parallel with catecholamine systems [123]; they were found to respond to an acute injection of nicotine (1 mg/kg s.c.) by an increase of 5-HIAA, while chronic drug exposure [according to the schedule described by Ribary and Lichtensteiger, 81] did not result in changes of this metabolite at GD 18 or PN 15. Hence, the involvement of this system remains uncertain and would need to be reexamined. Single daily injections of nicotine during pregnancy and lactation have recently been reported to increase postnatal somatostatin levels (frontoparietal cortex and hippocampus) and to decrease the number of the corresponding receptors, the effect had disappeared at PN 30 [135].

It should be noted that prenatal exposure to nicotine also causes changes in peripheral sympathetic function (see below) and in neuromuscular development [136]; these may represent a combination of central, peripheral and possibly endocrine effects.

Changes in Drug Sensitivity

Transient or lasting changes in drug-sensitivity represent a potentially important consequence of developmental drug exposure. They may concern the class of drugs to which the substance administered in pregnancy belongs, or other types of drugs through indirect effects on other transmitter systems. Evidence for such changes has been obtained, e.g. after prenatal exposure to ethanol [137 – 139] and benzodiazepines [140]. An increased sensitivity of the central nervous system (midbrain + brainstem) to nicotine has been demonstrated in prenatally nicotine-exposed rat offspring between PN 5 and PN 11, using ornithine decarboxylase, an enzyme which controls polyamine biosynthesis in the developing brain, as a parameter [141]. The observation indicates that the nicotinic receptors which are increased in number during the period examined are functional rather than desensitized (see above). This implies that effects of the drug itself but possibly also actions of endogenous acetylcholine would be enhanced at certain synapses during that period. The significance of the comparatively small changes in nicotinic receptor number persisting in certain brain regions at later stages, is difficult to assess at the present time. If the deficits were confined to a restricted number of neurons (or presynaptic terminals) in these areas, they would be proportionally greater and might be of functional importance. Delayed changes in (behavioral) responses to nicotine have also been reported after early *post*natal treatment with nicotine in mice [142].

In the peripheral nervous system, prenatal administration of nicotine has been found to lead to alterations in the sensitivity of β-adrenergic transmission [143, 144].

DNA Synthesis and Cell Proliferation

Chronic prenatal exposure to nicotine (or to tobacco smoke), or acute administration of the drug, results in changes in cell proliferation and cell death; it affects DNA, RNA and protein synthesis and the ontogenetic profile of ornithine decarboxylase, an enzyme involved in macromolecular synthesis [112, 145 – 148]. As in the case of effects on neurotransmitters or receptors, the changes outlast the period of drug exposure and differ between regions. It seems possible that such alterations in cell proliferation are due in part to nicotine-induced alterations in neurotransmitter systems; however, since organizational and trophic effects have been postulated for a number of different transmitters (acetylcholine, monoamines, GABA and others), the link with changes in specific transmitter systems remains as yet unclear. Moreover, other effects of the drug, e.g. on neuroendocrine systems (see below) or metabolism, could also influence cell proliferation [see also ref. no. 95].

Interactions with Neuroendocrine Brain Organization: Gonadal and Adrenal Axes

Sex-Linked Behavioral Effects

Interactions with developing neuroendocrine systems represent a potentially important mechanism by which centrally active drugs may affect brain development. Although compounds such as nicotine are known to affect adult neuroendocrine mechanisms [149], the possibility of actions on developing neuroendocrine systems so far seems to have received relatively little attention in humans. However, such effects have been documented for a number of psychoactive drugs in experimental animals. Most of the evidence relates to sexual brain differentiation, e.g. with regard to ethanol [150, 151], barbiturates [152, 153], cannabis [154], opiates [155], and nicotine [23, 156]. The pituitary-adrenal axis likewise undergoes an early period of organization which has been found to be drug-sensitive [139; see ref. no. 157 for a review]. The fetal adrenal axis is affected by nicotine in a sex-dependent way which points to the possibility of interactions between different developing hormone axes under the influence of drugs [77, see below].

When alterations in a process such as sexual brain differentiation are discussed as a possible pathogenetic mechanism for drug-induced defects in brain development, it is important to realize that sex differences exist in a great variety of brain functions besides sexual behavior, in mammals, e.g. in juvenile play behavior, activity patterns and physical energy expenditure, level of aggressiveness, taste preferences, feeding and body weight control, and cognitive functions. The latter are particular interesting insofar as relationships between sex and functional asymmetries of the two brain hemispheres are becoming increasingly apparent [158 – 161]. Sex-related interhemispheric differences of information processing (e.g., in relation to spatial, mathematical, verbal or musical capacities) are often linked with handedness in a complex way. If such functions were affected by prenatal drug exposure, a possible role of developmental alterations of a steroid hormone axis might at first not be directly evident.

In the rat where the main processes of sexual brain differentiation occur approximately during the last week of gestation and the 1st week of life, prenatal exposure to nicotine is followed by deficiencies in male characteristics of both reproductive and nonreproductive behavior. The treatment is followed by reduced male sexual behavior in adulthood [26, 123]; Segarra and Strand [123] also noted a reduction of adult testosterone levels. Prenatal nicotine exposure further abolishes sexual dimorphism of preference for sweet tastes [23]. Male rats normally exhibit a lower preference for saccharine solutions than females; after prenatal exposure to the drug, the mean saccharine preference of adult male offspring was raised to the level of their female littermates, while the taste preference of the latter did not differ from that of untreated control females. It should be noted that the level of preference was not the same in all animals of a given sex. In untreated controls, a high saccharine preference was observed in approximately one third of the males and two thirds of the females. Prenatal nicotine exposure shifted the proportion of males with a high preference to two thirds. This suggests that the drug effect may have involved some threshold mechanism.

Additional examples of sex-linked behavioral deficits encountered in laboratory animals and humans after prenatal exposure to nicotine, with a general preference for males, have been discussed in the section Behavioral Dysfunctions. In laboratory animals, they include the development of motor activity [25], rearing and initial activity in the open field [21] and active avoidance acquisition [22], in humans, reduced fetal growth [28], hyperactivity [9], and misbehavior [5].

Effects on Key Processes in the Developing Gonadal Axis

What are the mechanisms underlying these sex-linked functional alterations? In principle, the drug could directly interfere with a neuroendocrine axis of the developing organism, or act on developing sexually dimorphic brain structures. A considerable body of evidence supports the view that sexual brain differentiation depends on the secretion of testosterone during a critical phase of development [162]. However, it cannot be excluded that additional mechanisms such as control of neuronal phenotype by genetic sex might operate in certain systems. Some indication for the latter type of mechanism is provided by data on sex differences in dopamine cell cultures taken from fetuses at early developmental stages (GD 14 [127]). So far, the interpretation of these data resides on the assumption that sex steroid effects are absent before the well-known rise of testosterone at GD 18 (see below). Sex-dependent effects of nicotine such as those we observed in central catecholamine systems [81, see section Developmental Effects on Target Systems in the CNS], could be brought about by an interaction of the drug with both types of mechanisms. As interactions of nicotine with the expression of genetic sex of neurons presently remain speculative, we shall focus on sex steroid-dependent mechanisms of sexual brain differentiation which are directly affected by nicotine.

At about the time of onset of sexual brain differentiation, plasma testosterone of the male rat fetus rises to a peak at GD 18 [163]; at GD 19, it returns to a lower level but remains higher than in females during the following pre- and early postnatal days [164 – 168]. A prolonged increase of testosterone is also found in male human fetuses [169, 170].

Administration of nicotine (by osmotic minipump) to time-pregnant rats from GD 12 during 1 week, i.e. during the preparatory period and the early phase of sexual brain differentiation, suppressed the GD 18 testosterone peak but did not reduce plasma testosterone to female levels [23, 156]. Since the exact role of the testosterone peak is not known, it is not clear as yet how the drug-induced suppression of this peak would affect differentiation processes. Earlier data on prenatal stress effects [171] indicate that the GD 18 testosterone peak plays an essential part in male sexual brain differentiation of the rat. Analogous effects on fetal male plasma testosterone have also been reported for other centrally active drugs [157].

In addition to its effect on circulating testosterone, nicotine influences local steroid-dependent processes in the developing brain. Male sexual differentiation depends upon the local (intra-neuronal) aromatization of testosterone to estradiol which then binds to estrogen receptors [162, 172, 173]; this conversion has also been demonstrated in fetal primate brain [174]. The enzyme, aromatase, is present in the brain of both sexes. Enzyme activity becomes detectable in the diencephalon by GD 15 and reaches a peak at around GD 19 in males and females [175, 176]. This means that in the male fetus, high enzyme activity is present at the time of the testosterone peak and during the following days. The role of aromatase in the female brain remains unex-

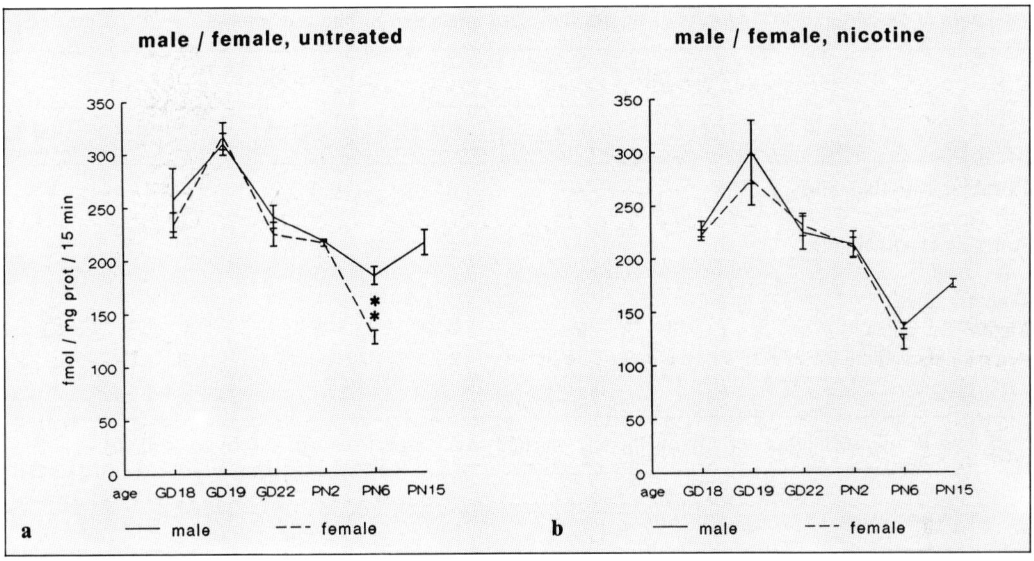

Fig. 3. Activity of aromatase, the enzyme converting androgens to estrogens, in forebrain of fetuses and offspring of untreated Long Evans rats (**a**) and of rats treated with nicotine by osmotic minipump (6 mg/kg/day) from GD 12 to GD 19 (**b**). In a tissue piece comprising preoptic area, hypothalamus and amygdala, enzyme activity rises to a peak at around GD 19; the two sexes differ at PN 6 **$p < 0.01$. This sex difference is abolished after prenatal nicotine treatment. An identical effect was obtained by a daily dose of 2 mg/kg. Mean values + SEM of individual animals from 4 – 8 litters; for additional control groups see Von Ziegler et al. [77].

plained. Sex differences in enzyme activity have been reported for certain stages of prenatal and postnatal development [77]. In a brain piece containing preoptic area, hypothalamus and amygdala, i.e. areas with high enzyme activity, we observed a sex difference at PN 6, towards the end of the critical period of sexual brain differentiation, with lower activity in females (fig. 3).

Prenatal administration of nicotine (6 or 2 mg/kg/day; GD 12 – 18/19) did not affect aromatase activity during drug exposure or shortly thereafter (GD 18, GD 19, GD 22, PN 2), but it was followed, at PN 6, by a reduction of enzyme activity in the male brain to the female level. The sex difference normally existing at that stage was thus completely abolished (fig. 3) [77]. The delayed effect on enzyme activity might result either from a change in the development (e.g., proliferation rate or cell death) of some nerve cell population(s) expressing aromatase, or from a delayed change in the expression of the enzyme. As mentioned above, changes in cell proliferation and maturation have been observed in brain after prenatal nicotine exposure [146].

A detailed analysis of the pre- and postnatal development of aromatase activity in individual rat brain areas of the two hemispheres, undertaken in a search for a developmental basis of neuroendocrine asymmetries, has recently revealed a more complex picture [177]. The developmental patterns of aroma-

Table 3. Developmental patterns of hemispheric dominance in aromatase activity

	Male rats			Female rats		
	GD 22	PN 6	PN 15	GD 22	PN 6	PN 15
Posterior hypothalamus	R	=	=	=	=	= (L)
Anterior hypothalamus	L	R	=	= (R)	L	L
Preoptic area	L	=	L	=	=	=
Medial amygdala	L	R	=	R	L	L
Anterior amygdala	= (L)	=	R	=	R	L

L and R indicate higher activity on the left or right side, respectively ($p < 0.01$ to < 0.05).

tase activity differ between regions and between sexes and exhibit marked differences between the left and right side (table 3). In the male, the development of asymmetry of aromatase activity could tentatively be interpreted as a left to right shift of hemispheric dominance proceeding in a caudorostral direction. Whether these patterns result from differences in the expression of aromatase or in the number of cells expressing the enzyme is presently being investigated.

It is quite evident that the action of nicotine should be viewed against the background of this regional complexity. Effects of the drug on the development of cell groups containing aromatase or on the expression of the enzyme could produce regionally different effects at different stages of development. In this way, the drug could interfere in a complex manner with regional development and the generation of hemispheric asymmetries, including cortical functions as a consequence of developmental interactions between subcortical and cortical areas. Functions linked with hemispheric asymmetries should thus be considered in the context of developmental actions of nicotine, in particular if they exhibit sex differences. In this respect, the impaired development of verbal skills is interesting. More recently, a shift of handedness towards the ambidextrous state has been described in young adults whose mothers smoked during pregnancy [178]. In both cases, no sex differences in the effect of nicotine have so far been detected.

The mechanisms underlying the effects on fetal testosterone levels and postnatal aromatase activity are not known; the two effects might possibly be related to each other. The depression of the fetal testosterone peak might affect the development of some neuron group or influence aromatase expression. In adult rats, androgens influence aromatase levels by enzyme induction [179, 180]. Whether this is also true for the fetus remains uncertain, however, since aromatase induction by androgens was not seen in the brain of the fetal ferret [181].

Sex-Linked Changes in the Developing Adrenal Axis

Developmental signals may also arise from other endocrine systems. Two sets of data point to an involvement of the adrenal axis where effects of nicotine are well documented for the adult organism [149]. At the GD 18 stage when the testosterone peak is suppressed [23], plasma corticosterone was significantly increased in male fetuses exposed to nicotine (by osmotic minipump) from GD 12 [77]. No effect was seen in female fetuses and in pregnant dams at that time. By PN 15, male corticosterone had returned to normal levels. Such a transient enhancement of corticosterone secretion could affect a variety of development processes; it might also influence aromatase-expressing neuron groups in a sensitive developmental phase. With a different treatment schedule – intraperitoneal injections of nicotine throughout pregnancy – a different type of functional alteration was observed [182], i.e., a delayed increase of plasma ACTH at PN 15 (in a combined analysis of male and female samples). While these data are not directly comparable to our findings, they further support the idea of an interaction of nicotine with the developing adrenal axis.

These observations on gonadal and adrenal axis illustrate that interactions with developing neuroendocrine systems represent a potentially important factor in developmental actions of nicotine. Alterations in neuroendocrine ontogeny have been reported for other psychoactive drugs [157]. They may involve a great variety of functions and deserve to receive more attention in the future.

Acknowledgements

The investigations of the authors reported herein have been supported by several grants of the Swiss National Science Foundation. The authors wish to acknowledge the most valuable contributions of their colleagues who are coauthors in the various studies reviewed in this article.

References

1 Kelly J, Mathews KA, O'Conor M: Smoking in pregnancy: Effects on mother and fetus. Br J Obstet Gynaecol 1984;91:111–117.
2 Davie R, Butler N, Goldstein H: From Birth to Seven: The Second Report of the National Child Development Study (1958 Cohort). Longman in Association with the National Children's Bureau. Clowes, London, 1972.
3 Butler NR, Goldstein H: Smoking in pregnancy and subsequent child development. Br Med J 1973;4:573–575.
4 Denson R, Nanson JL, McWatters MA: Hyperkinesis and maternal smoking. Can Psychiatr Assoc J 1975;20:183–187.
5 Dunn HG, McBurney AK, Ingram S, Hunter CM: Maternal cigarette smoking during pregnancy and the child's subsequent development. II Neurological and intellectual maturation to the age of 6 1/2 years. Can J Public Health 1977;68:43–50.
6 Saxton DW: The behaviour of infants whose mothers smoke in pregnancy. Early Hum Dev 1978;2:363–369.
7 Picone TA, Allen LH, Olsen PN: Pregnancy outcome in North American women. II. Effects of diet, cigarette smoking, stress and weight gain on placentas, and on neonatal physical and behavioral characteristics. Am J Clin Nutr 1983;36: 1214–1224.
8 Rantakallio P: A follow-up study up to the age of 14 of children whose mothers smoked during pregnancy. Acta Paediatr Scand 1983;72:747–753.
9 Naeye RL, Peters EC: Mental development of children whose mothers smoked during pregnancy. Obstet Gynecol 1984;64:601–607.
10 Fried PA, Makin JE: Neonatal behavioral correlates of prenatal exposure to marijuana, cigarettes, and alcohol in a low risk population. Neurobehav Toxicol Teratol 1987;9:1–7.
11 Fried PA, Watkinson B, Dillon RF: Neonatal neurological status in a low-risk population after prenatal exposure to cigarettes, marijuana, and alcohol. J Dev Behav Pediatr 1987;8:318–326.
12 Fried PA, Watkinson B: 12-and 24-month neurobehavioral follow-up of children prenatally exposed to marijuana, cigarettes and alcohol. Neurotoxicol Teratol 1988;10:305–313.
13 Fried PA, Watkinson B: 36- and 48-month neurobehavioral follow-up of children prenatally

exposed to marijuana, cigarettes, and alcohol. J Dev Behav Pediatr 1990;11:49–58.
14 Makin J, Fried PA, Watkinson B: A comparison of active and passive smoking during pregnancy: Long-term effects. Neurotoxicol Teratol 1991;13: 5–12.
15 Manning F, Walker D, Feyerabend C: The effect of nicotine on fetal breathing movements in conscious pregnant ewes. Obstet Gynecol 1978;52: 563–568.
16 Martin JC, Becker RF: The effects of nicotine administration in utero upon activity in the rat. Psychon Sc 1970;19:59–60.
17 Martin JC, Becker RF: The effect of maternal nicotine absorption or hypoxic episodes upon appetitive behavior of rat offspring. Dev Psychobiol 1971;4:133–147.
18 Hudson DB, Meisami E, Timiras PS: Brain development in offspring of rats treated with nicotine during pregnancy. Experientia 1973;29:286–288.
19 Peters DAV, Taub H, Tang S: Postnatal effects of maternal nicotine exposure. Neurobehav Toxicol 1979;1:221–225.
20 Johns JM, Louis TM, Becker RF, Means LW: Behavioral effects of prenatal exposure to nicotine in guinea pigs. Neurobehav Toxicol Teratol 1982; 4:365–369.
21 Peters DAV, Tang S: Sex-dependent biological changes following prenatal nicotine exposure in the rat. Pharmacol Biochem Behav 1982;17: 1077–1082.
22 Genedani S, Bernardi M, Bertolini A: Sex-linked differeces in avoidance learning in the offspring of rats treated with nicotine during pregnancy. Psychopharmacology 1983;80:93–95.
23 Lichtensteiger W, Schlumpf M: Prenatal nicotine affects fetal testosterone and sexual dimorphism of saccharin preference. Pharmacol Biochem Behav 1985;23:439–444.
24 Fung YK: Postnatal behavioural effects of maternal nicotine exposure in rats. J Pharm Pharmacol 1988;40:870–872.
25 Schlumpf M, Gähwiler M, Ribary U, Lichtensteiger W: A new device for monitoring early motor development: Prenatal nicotine-induced changes. Pharmacol Biochem Behav 1988;30:199–203.
26 Segarra AC, Strand FL: Perinatal administration of nicotine alters subsequent sexual behavior and testosterone levels of male rats. Brain Res 1989; 480:151–159.
27 Baer DS, McClearn GE, Wilson JR: Fertility, maternal care, and offspring behavior in mice prenatally treated with tobacco smoke. Dev Psychobiol 1980;13:643–652.
28 Wertelecki W, Hoff C, Zansky S: Maternal smoking: Greater effect on males, fetal tobacco syndrome? Teratology 1987;35:317–320.
29 Longo LD: The biological effects of carbon monoxide on the pregnant woman, fetus and the newborn infant. Am J Obstet Gynecol 1977;129:69–103.
30 Astrup P, Olsen HM, Trolle D: Effect of moderate carbon monoxide exposure on fetal development. Lancet 1975;ii:1220–1222.
31 Fechter LD, Annau Z: Toxicity of mild prenatal carbon monoxide exposure. Science 1977;197: 680–682.
32 Tachi N, Aoyama M: Postnatal growth in rats prenatally exposed to cigarette smoke or carbon monoxide. Bull Environ Contam Toxicol 1990; 45:641–648.
33 Wouters EJM, de Jong PA, Cornelissen PJH, Kurver PHJ, van Oel WC, van Woensel CLM: Smoking and low birthweight: Absence of influence by carbon monoxide? Eur J Obstet Gynecol Reprod Biol 1987;5:35–41.
34 Lindblad A, Marsal K, Andersson K-E: Effect of nicotine on human fetal blood flow. Obstet Gynecol 1988;72:371–382.
35 Suzuki K, Horiguchi T, Comas-Urrutia AC, Mueller-Heubach E, Morishima H, Adamsons K: Placental transfer and distribution of nicotine in the pregnant rhesus monkey. Am J Obstet Gynecol 1974;119:253–262.
36 Luck W, Nau H, Hansen R, Steldinger R: Extent of nicotine and cotinine transfer to the human fetus, placenta and amniotic fluid of smoking mothers. Dev Pharmacol Ther 1985;8:384–395.
37 Lehtovirta P, Forss M: The acute effect of smoking on intervillous blood flow of the placenta. Br J Obstet Gynaecol 1978;85:729–731.
38 Philipp K, Pateisky N, Endler M: Effects of smoking on uteroplacental blood flow. Gynecol Obstet Invest 1984;17:179–182.
39 Vitting AK, Hermann N: Placenta flow reduction in pregnant smokers. Acta Obstet Gynecol Scand 1984;63:707–709.
40 Resnik R, Conover WB, Key TC, Van Vunakis H: Uterine blood flow and catecholamine response to repetitive nicotine exposure in the pregnant ewe. Am J Obstet Gynecol 1985;151:885–891.

41 Morrow RJ, Ritchie JWK, Bull SB: Maternal cigarette smoking: The effects on umbilical and uterine blood flow velocity. Am J Obstet Gynecol 1988;159:1069 – 1071.

42 Asmussen I: Ultrastructure of human umbilical veins. Observations on veins from newborn children of smoking and nonsmoking mothers. Acta Obstet Gynecol Scand 1978;57:253 – 255.

43 Asmussen I: Ultrastructure of the villi and fetal capillaries in placentas from smoking and nonsmoking mothers. Br J Obstet Gynaecol 1980;87: 239 – 245.

44 Burton GJ, Palmer ME, Dalton KJ: Morphometric differences between the placental vasculature of non-smokers, smokers and ex-smokers. Br J Obstet Gynaecol 1989;96:907 – 915.

45 Critchley GR, Burton GJ: Intra-lobular variations in barrier thickness in the mature human placenta. Placenta 1987;8:185 – 194.

46 Jackson MR, Mayhew TM, Haas JT: Morphometric studies on villi in human term placentae and the effects of altitude, ethnic grouping and sex of newborn. Placenta 1987;8:487 – 495.

47 Porter KB, Goldhamer R, Mankad A, Peevy K, Gaddy J, Spinnato JA: Evaluation of arterial oxygen saturation in pregnant patients and their newborns. Obstet Gynecol 1988;71:354 – 357

48 Sindberg Eriksen P, Marsal K: Circulatory changes in the fetal aorta after maternal smoking. Br J Obstet Gynaecol 1987;94:301 – 305.

49 Jouppila P, Kirkinen P, Eik-Nes S: Acute effect of maternal smoking on the human fetal blood flow. Br J Obstet Gynaecol 1983;90:7 – 10.

50 Pijpers L, Wladimiroff JW, McGhie JS, Bom N: Acute effect of maternal smoking on the maternal and fetal cardiovascular system. Early Hum Dev 1984;10:95 – 105.

51 Suzuki K, Minei LJ, Johnson EE: Effect of nicotine upon uterine blood flow in the pregnant rhesus monkey. Am J Obstet Gynecol 1980;136: 1009 – 1013.

52 Quigley ME, Sheehan KL, Wilkes MM, Yen SSC: Effects of maternal smoking on circulating catecholamine levels and fetal heart rates. Am J Obstet Gynecol 1979;133:685 – 690.

53 Wennmalm A: Interaction of nicotine and prostaglandins in the cardiovascular system. Prostaglandins 1982;23:139 – 144.

54 Ahlsten G, Ewald U, Tuvemo T: Maternal smoking reduces prostacyclin formation in human umbilical arteries. A study on strictly selected pregnancies. Acta Obstet Gynecol Scand 1986; 65:645 – 649.

55 Ahlsten G, Ewald U, Tuvemo T: Prostacyclin-like activity in umbilical arteries is dose-dependently reduced by maternal smoking and related to nicotine levels. Biol Neonate 1990;58:271 – 278.

56 Stoel I, van der Giessen WJ, Zwolsman E, Verheugt FWA, ten Hoor F, Quadt FJA, Hagenholtz DG: Effect of nicotine on production of prostacyclin in human umbilical artery. Br Heart J 1982;48:493 – 496.

57 Busacca M, Balconi G, Pietra A, Vergara-Dauden M, de Gaetano G, Dejana E: Maternal smoking and prostacyclin production by cultured endothelial cells from umbilical arteries. Am J Obstet Gynecol 1984;148:1127 – 1130.

58 Alster P, Wennmalm A: Effect of nicotine on prostacyclin formation in rat aorta. Eur J Pharmacol 1983;86:441 – 446.

59 Karbowski B, Bauch H-J, Schneider HPG: Funktionelle Differenzierung des vaskulären Endothels bei Hochrisikoschwangerschaften. Z Geburtshilfe Perinatol 1989;193:8 – 12.

60 Chahine R, Kaiser R, Pham Huu Chanh A: Effects of nicotine and cotinine on prostacyclin biosynthesis; in Adlkofer F, Thurau K (eds): Effects of Nicotine on Biological Systems. Advances in Pharmacological Sciences. Basel, Birkhäuser, 1991, pp 171 – 175.

61 Goerig M, Ullrich V, Schettler G, Foltis C, Habenicht A: A new role for nicotine: Selective inhibition of thromboxane formation by direct interaction with thromboxane synthase; in Adlkofer F, Thurau K (eds): Effects of Nicotine on Biological Systems. Advances in Pharmacological Sciences. Basel, Birkhäuser, 1991, 165 – 170.

62 Raulf M, König W: Effects of nicotine on the generation of lipoxygenase products; in Adlkofer F, Thurau K (eds): Effects of Nicotine on Biological Systems. Advances in Pharmacological Sciences. Basel, Birkhäuser, 1991, pp 177 – 181.

63 Uedelhoven WM, Rützel A, Meese CO, Weber PC: Smoking alters thromboxane metabolism in man. Biochim Biophys Acta 1991;1081:197 – 201.

64 Tuvemo T: Role of prostaglandins, prostacyclin, and thromboxanes in the control of the umbilical-placental circulation. Semin Perinatol 1980;4: 91 – 95.

65 Makila UM, Jouppila P, Kirkinen P, Viinikka L:

Relation between umbilical prostacyclin production and blood-flow in the fetus. Lancet 1983;i: 728–729.
66 Van Hattum B, de Voogt P, Copius Peereboom JW: Cadmium content of human placenta. Int J Environ Anal Chem 1981;10:121–133.
67 Copius Peereboom-Stegeman JHJ, van der Velde WJ, Dessing JWM: Influence of cadmium on placental structure. Ecotoxicol Environ Safety 1983;7:79–86.
68 Kuhnert BR, Kuhnert PM, Debanne S, Williams TG: The relationship between cadmium, zinc, and birth weight in pregnant women who smoke. Am J Obstet Gynecol 1987;157:1247–1251.
69 Jensen OH, Foss OP: Smoking in pregnancy: Effects of the birth weight and on thiocyanate concentration in mother and baby. Acta Obstet Gynecol Scand 1981;60:177–181.
70 Rowell PP, Leventer SM, Clark MJ: The effect of cigarette smoking during pregnancy on the cholinergic system in isolated term human placental tissue. Biol Reprod 1986;34:344–348.
71 Rama Sastry BV: Placental toxicology: Tobacco smoke, abused drugs, multiple chemical interactions, and placental function. Reprod Fertil Dev 1991;3:355–372.
72 Mochizuki M, Maruo T, Masuko K, Ohtsu T: Effects of smoking on fetoplacental-maternal system during pregnancy. Am J Obstet Gynecol 1984;149: 413–420.
73 Nebert DW, Winker J, Gelboin HV: Aryl hydrocarbon hydroxylase activity in human placenta from smoking and nonsmoking women. Cancer Res 1969;29:1763–1769.
74 Manchester DK, Parker NB, Bowman CM: Maternal smoking increases xenobiotic metabolism in placenta but not umbilical vein endothelium. Pediatr Res 1984;18:1071–1075.
75 Slotkin TA, Orband-Miller L, Queen KL, Whitmore WL, Seidler FJ: Effects of prenatal nicotine exposure on biochemical development of rat brain regions: Maternal drug infusions via osmotic minipumps. J Pharmacol Exp Ther 1987;240: 602–611.
76 Murrin LC, Ferrer JR, Zeug W, Haley NJ: Nicotine administration to rats: Methodological considerations. Life Sci 1987;40:1699–1708.
77 Von Ziegler NI, Schlumpf M, Lichtensteiger W: Prenatal nicotine exposure selectively affects perinatal forebrain aromatase activity and fetal adrenal function in male rats. Dev Brain Res 1991;62:23–31.
78 Isaac PF, Rand MJ: Cigarette smoking and plasma levels of nicotine. Nature 1972;236:308–310.
79 Hill P, Haley NJ, Wynder EL: Cigarette smoking: Carboxyhemoglobin, plasma nicotine, cotinine and thiocyanate vs self-reported smoking data and cardiovascular disease. J Chronic Dis 1983;36: 439–449.
80 Benowitz NL, Jacob P III: Nicotine and carbon monoxide intake from high-and low-yield cigarettes. Clin Pharmacol Ther 1984;36:265–270.
81 Ribary U, Lichtensteiger W: Effects of acute and chronic prenatal nicotine treatment on central catecholamine systems of male and female rat fetuses and offspring. J Pharmacol Exp Ther 1989; 248:786–791.
82 Navarro HA, Seidler FJ, Schwartz RD, Baker FE, Dobbins SS, Slotkin TA: Prenatal exposure to nicotine impairs nervous system development at a dose which does not affect viability or growth. Brain Res Bull 1989;23:187–192.
83 Fung YK, Lau YS: Effects of prenatal nicotine exposure on rat striatal dopaminergic and nicotinic systems. Pharmacol Biochem Behav 1989;33: 1–6.
84 Barbieri RL, Friedman AJ, Osathanondh R: Cotinine and nicotine inhibit human fetal adrenal 11β-hydroxylase. J Clin Endocrinol Metab 1989; 69:1221–1224.
85 Romano C, Goldstein A: Stereospecific nicotine receptors on rat brain membranes. Science 1980; 210:647–649.
86 Marks MJ, Stitzel JA, Romm E, Wehner JM, Collins AC: Nicotinic binding sites in rat and mouse brain: Comparison of acetylcholine, nicotine and alpha-bungarotoxin. Mol Pharmacol 1986;30: 427–436.
87 Wonnacott S: Brain nicotine binding sites. Human Toxicol 1987;6:343–353.
88 Deneris ES, Connolly J, Rogers SW, Duvoisin R: Pharmacological and functional diversity of neuronal nicotinic acetylcholine receptors. Trend Pharmacol Sci 1991;12:34–40.
89 Wonnacott S: Alpha-bungarotoxin binds to low-affinity binding sites in rat brain. J Neurochem 1986;47:1706–1712.
90 Clarke PBS, Schwartz RD, Paul SM, Pert CB, Pert A: Nicotinic binding in rat brain: Autoradiographic comparison of ^{3}H-acetylcholine, ^{3}H-

nicotine, ^{125}I-α-bungarotoxin. J Neurosci 1985; 5:1307–1315.

91 Fiedler EP, Marks MJ, Collins AC: Postnatal development of two nicotinic cholinergic receptors in seven mouse brain regions. Int J Dev Neurosci 1990;8:533–540.

92 Larsson C, Nordberg A, Falkeborn Y, Lundberg PA: Regional [^{3}H]-acetylcholine and [^{3}H]-nicotine binding in developing mouse brain. Int J Dev Neurosci 1985;3:667–671.

93 Yamada S, Kagawa Y, Isogai M, Takayanagi N, Hayashi E: Ontogenesis of nicotinic acetylcholine receptors and presynaptic cholinergic neurons in mammalian brain. Life Sci 1985;138:637–644.

94 Sugiyama H, Hagino N, Moore G, Lee JW: [^{3}H]-nicotine binding sites in developing fetal brain in rats. Neurosci Res 1985;2:387–392.

95 Lichtensteiger W, Ribary U, Schlumpf M, Odermatt B, Widmer HR: Prenatal adverse effects of nicotine on the developing brain. Prog Brain Res 1988;73:137–157.

96 Schlumpf M, Naeff B, Lichtensteiger W: Characteristics of neurotransmitter receptor development in the fetus; in Rosén KG, Lagercrantz H (eds): Research Trends in Fetal Physiology. Gothenburg, University of Gothenburg, 1990, pp 83–86.

97 Naeff B, Schlumpf M, Lichtensteiger W: Pre-and postnatal development of high-affinity [3H] nicotine binding sites in rat brain regions: An autoradiographic study. Dev Brain Res 1992; 68:163–174.

98 Schlumpf M, Palacios JM, Cortes R, Lichtensteiger W: Regional development of muscarinic cholinergic binding sites in the prenatal rat brain. Neuroscience 1991;45:347–357.

99 Cairns NJ, Wonnacott S: [^{3}H](–)nicotine binding sites in human fetal brain. Brain Res 1988;475:1–7.

100 Schlumpf M, Lichtensteiger W: Benzodiazepine and muscarinic cholinergic binding sites in striatum and brainstem of the human fetus. Int J Dev Neurosci 1987;5:283–287.

101 Marin-Padilla M: Dual origin of the mammalian neocortex and evolution of the cortical plate. Anat Embryol 1978;152:109–126.

102 Chun JJ, Nakamura MJ, Shatz CJ: Transient cells of the developing mammalian telencephalon are peptide-immunoreactive neurons. Nature 1987;325:617–620.

103 Bayer SA, Altman J: Neocortical Development. New York, Raven Press, 1991.

104 Kristt DA, Molliver ME: Synapses in newborn rat cerebral cortex: A quantitative ultrastructural study. Brain Res 1976;108:180–186.

105 Schlumpf M, Bruinink A, Lichtensteiger W, Cortés R, Palacios JM, Pazos A: Beta-adrenergic binding sites in fetal rat central nervous system and pineal gland: Their relation to other receptor sites. Dev Pharmacol Ther 1987;10:422–435.

106 Schlumpf M, Shoemaker WJ, Bloom FE: Innervation of embryonic rat cerebral cortex by catecholamine-containing fibers. J Comp Neurol 1980;192:361–376.

107 Koh S, Loy R: Localization and development of nerve growth factor-sensitive rat basal forebrain neurons and their afferent projections to hippocampus and neocortex. J Neurosci 1989;9: 2999–3018.

108 Friauf E, McConnell SK, Shatz CJ: Functional synaptic circuits in the subplate during fetal and early postnatal development of cat visual cortex. J Neurosci 1990;10:2601–2613.

109 Hohmann CF, Brooks AR, Coyle JT: Neonatal lesions of the basal forebrain cholinergic neurons result in abnormal cortical development. Dev Brain Res 1988;42:253–264.

110 Sofroniew MV, Pearson RCA, Powell TPS: The cholinergic nuclei of the basal forebrain of the rat: Normal structure, development and experimentally induced degeneration. Brain Res 1987;411:310–331.

111 Navarro HA, Seidler FJ, Eylers JP, Baker FE, Dobbins SS, Lappi SE, Slotkin TA: Effects of prenatal nicotine exposure on development of central and peripheral cholinergic neurotransmitter systems. Evidence for cholinergic trophic influences in developing brain. J Pharmacol Exp Ther 1989;251:894–900.

112 Sershen H, Reith MEA, Banay-Schwartz M, Lajtha A: Effects of prenatal administration of nicotine on amino acid pools, protein metabolism, and nicotine binding in the brain. Neurochem Res 1982;7:1515–1522.

113 Hagino N, Lee JW: Effect of maternal nicotine on the development of sites for [^{3}H]nicotine binding in the fetal brain. Int J Dev Neurosci 1985; 3:567–571.

114 Slotkin TA, Orband-Miller L, Queen KL: Development of [^{3}H]nicotine binding sites in brain

regions of rats exposed to nicotine prenatally via maternal injections or infusions. J Pharmacol Exp Ther 1987;242:232–237.
115 Naeff-Odermatt B, Schlumpf M, Lichtensteiger W: Effect of prenatal nicotine exposure on central nicotinic binding sites at different stages of development. Experientia 1990;46:A81.
116 Naeff-Odermatt B: Effect of Prenatal Nicotine Exposure on the Development of Nicotinic Cholinergic Binding Sites in Rat Brain Regions; thesis No 9371, Eidgenössische Technische Hochschule, Zürich, 1991.
117 Marks MJ, Burch JB, Collins AC: Effects of chronic nicotine infusion on tolerance development and nicotinic receptors. J Pharmacol Exp Ther 1983;226:817–825.
118 Schwartz RD, Kellar KJ: Nicotinic cholinergic receptor binding sites in the brain: Regulation in vivo. Science 1983;220:214–216.
119 Schlumpf M, Lichtensteiger W, Shoemaker WJ, Bloom FE: Fetal monoamine systems: Early stages and cortical projections; in Parvez J, Parvez S (eds): Biogenic Amines in Development. Amsterdam, Elsevier, 1980, pp 567–590.
120 Lichtensteiger W, Felix D, Lienhart R, Hefti F: A quantitative correlation between single unit activity and fluorescence intensity of dopamine neurons in zona compacta of substantia nigra, as demonstrated under the influence of nicotine and physostigmine. Brain Res 1976;117:85–103.
121 Lichtensteiger W, Hefti F, Felix D, Huwyler T, Melamed E, Schlumpf M: Stimulation of nigrostriatal dopamine neurons by nicotine. Neuropharmacology 1982;21:963–968.
122 Egan TM, North RA: Actions of acetylcholine and nicotine on rat locus coeruleus neurons in vitro. Neuroscience 1986;19:565–571.
123 Ribary U: Nicotine in Pregnancy: Acute and Persistant Effects on Central Monoaminergic Systems in Rat Fetus and Offspring; thesis No 7939, Federal Institute of Technology, Zürich, 1985.
124 Slotkin TA, Cho H, Whitmore WL: Effects of prenatal nicotine exposure on neuronal development: Selective actions on central and peripheral catecholaminergic pathways. Brain Res Bull 1987;18:601–611.
125 Navarro HA, Seidler FJ, Whitmore WL, Slotkin TA: Prenatal exposure to nicotine via maternal infusions: Effects on development of catecholamine systems. J Pharmacol Exp Ther 1988;244: 940–944.
126 Engele J, Pilgrim C, Reisert I: Sexual differentiation of mesencephalic dopaminergic neurons in vitro: Effects of sex and gonadal hormones. Int J Dev Neurosci 1989;7:603–611.
127 Reisert I, Pilgrim C: Sexual differentiation of monoaminergic neurons – Genetic or epigenetic? Trends Neurosci 1991;14:468–473.
128 Reisert I, Schuster R, Zienecker R, Pilgrim C: Prenatal development of mesencephalic and diencephalic dopaminergic systems in the male and female rat. Dev Brain Res 1990;53:222–229.
129 Navarro HA, Slotkin TA, Tayyeb MI, Lappi SE, Seidler FJ: Effects of fetal nicotine exposure on development of adrenergic receptor binding in rat brain regions: Selective changes in α_1-receptors. Rcs Commun Subst Abuse 1990;11:95–103.
130 Peters DAV: Prenatal nicotine exposure increases adrenergic receptor binding in the rat cerebral cortex. Res Commun Chem Pathol Pharmacol 1984;46:307–317.
131 Raskin LA, Shaywitz BA, Shaywitz SE, Cohen JD, Anderson GM: Early brain damage and attention deficit disorder: An animal model; in Almly CR, Finger S (eds): Early Brain Damage. Orlando, Academic Press, 1984, vol 1, pp 111–125.
132 Imperato A, Mulas A, Di Chiara G: Nicotine preferentially stimulates dopamine release in the limbic system of freely moving rats. Eur J Pharmacol 1986;132:337–338.
133 Belmont L: Epidemiology; in Rie HE, Rie ED (eds): Handbook of Minimal Brain Dysfunctions. New York, Wiley, 1980, pp 55–74.
134 Helper MM: Follow-up of children with minimal brain dysfunctions: Outcomes and predictors; in Rie HE, Rie ED (eds): Handbook of Minimal Brain Dysfunctions. New York, Wiley, 1980, pp 75–114.
135 Barrios V, Rodriguez-Sanchez MN, Arilla E: Effect of maternal exposure to nicotine on level and binding of somatostatin in brain of developing offspring. Neuropharmacology 1991;30:579–584.
136 Rose KJ, Strand FL: Accelerated neuromuscular development in the rat with prenatal exposure to nicotine. Int J Dev Neurosci 1990;8:565–573.
137 Abel EL, Bush R, Dintcheff BA: Exposure of rats to alcohol in utero alters drug sensitivity in adulthood. Science 1981;212:1531–1533.

138 Taylor AN, Liu SH, Randolph D, Branch BJ, Kokka N: Fetal exposure to ethanol alters drug sensitivity in adult rats. Alcoholism 1981;5:169.
139 Taylor AN, Branch BJ, Kokka N, Poland RE: Neonatal and long-term neuroendocrine effects of fetal alcohol exposure. Monogr Neural Sci 1983;9:140–152.
140 Schlumpf M, Ramseier H, Abriel H, Youmbi M, Baumann JB, Lichtensteiger W: Diazepam effects on the fetus. Neurotoxicology 1989;10:501–516.
141 Slotkin TA, Lappi SE, Tayyeb MI, Seidler FJ: Chronic prenatal nicotine exposure sensitizes rat brain to acute postnatal nicotine challenge as assessed with ornithine decarboxylase. Life Sci 1991;49:665–670.
142 Nordberg A, Zhang X, Fredriksson A, Eriksson P: Neonatal nicotine exposure induces permanent changes in brain nicotinic receptors and behaviour in adult mice. Dev Brain Res 1991;63:201–207.
143 Navarro HA, Mills E, Seidler FJ, Baker FE, Lappi SE, Tayyeb MI, Spencer JR, Slotkin TA: Prenatal nicotine exposure impairs β-adrenergic function: Persistent chronotrophic subsensitivity despite recovery from deficits in receptor binding. Brain Res Bull 1990;25:233–237.
144 Slotkin TA, Navarro HA, McCook EC, Seidler FJ: Fetal nicotine exposure produces postnatal up-regulation of adenylate cyclase activity in peripheral tissues. Life Sci 1990;48:1561–1567.
145 Krous HF, Campbell GA, Fowler MW, Catron AC, Farber JP: Maternal nicotine administration and fetal brainstem damage: A rat model with implications for sudden infant death syndrome. Am J Obstet Gynecol 1981;140:743–746.
146 Slotkin TA, Greer N, Faust J, Cho H, Seidler FJ: Effects of maternal nicotine injections on brain development in the rat: Ornithine decarboxylase activity, nucleic acids and proteins in discrete brain regions. Brain Res Bull 1986;17:41–50.
147 Kleshcheva RP: Changes in the sensorimotor cortex of offspring after chronic intoxication by tobacco smoke through the mother-fetus system. Neurosci Behav Physiol 1990;20:95–97.
148 McFarland BJ, Seidler FJ, Slotkin TA: Inhibition of DNA synthesis in neonatal rat brain regions caused by acute nicotine administration. Dev Brain Res 1991;58:223–229.
149 Lichtensteiger W: Interaction of acetylcholine in neuroendocrine function; in Vincent J-D, Kordon C (eds): Cell Biology of Hypothalamic Neurosecretion. Paris, Editions du CNRS, 1978, pp 179–191.
150 Kakihana R, Butte JC, Moore JA: Endocrine effects of maternal alcoholization: Plasma and brain testosterone, dihydrotestosterone, estradiol, and corticosterone. Alcohol Clin Exp Res 1980;4: 57–61.
151 McGivern RF, Clancy AN, Hill MA, Noble EP: Prenatal alcohol exposure alters adult expression of sexually dimorphic behavior in the rat. Science 1984;224:896–898.
152 Gupta C, Yaffe SJ, Shapiro BH: Prenatal exposure to phenobarbital permanently decreases testosterone and causes reproductive dysfunction. Science 1982;216:640–642.
153 Reinisch JM, Sanders SA: Early barbiturate exposure: The brain, sexually dimorphic behavior, and learning. Neurosci Biobehav Rev 1982;6: 311–319.
154 Dalterio S, Bartke A: Fetal testosterone in mice: Effect of gestational age and cannabinoid exposure. J Endocrinol 1981;91:509–514.
155 Ward OB, Orth JM, Weisz J: A possible role of opiates in modifying sexual differentiation. Monogr Neural Sci 1983;9:194–200.
156 Lichtensteiger W, Schlumpf M: Steroids and neurotransmitter mechanisms in the prenatal brain; in Fuxe K, Gustavsson J-A, Wetterberg L (eds): Steroid Hormone Regulation of the Brain. Oxford, Pergamon Press, 1981, pp 161–172.
157 Lichtensteiger W, Schlumpf M: Prenatal neuropharmacology: Implications for neuroendocrine development; in Ellendorf F, Gluckman PD, Parvizi N (eds): Ithaca, Perinatology Press, 1984, vol 2: Fetal Neuroendocrinology, pp 59–70.
158 Geschwind N, Behan P: Left-handedness: Association with immune disease, migraine, and developmental learning disorder. Proc Natl Acad Sci USA, 1982;79:5097–5100.
159 Benbow CP, Benbow RM: Biological correlates of high mathematical reasoning ability; in De Vries GJ, De Bruin JPG, Uylings HBM, Corner MA (eds): Prog Brain Res. Amsterdam, Elsevier, 1984;61:469–490.
160 Heister G: Sex differences in visual half-field superiority as a function of responding hand and motor demands; in De Vries GJ, De Bruin JPC, Uylings HBM, Corner MA (eds): Prog Brain Res. Amsterdam, Elsevier, 1984;61:457–468.
161 Hassler M: Functional cerebral asymmetries and

cognitive abilities in musicians, painters, and controls. Brain Cogn 1990;13:1 – 17.
162 Goy RW, McEwen BS: Sexual Differentiation of the Brain. Cambridge, MIT Press, 1980.
163 Weisz J, Ward IL: Plasma testosterone and progesterone titers of pregnant rats, their male and female fetuses, and neonatal offspring. Endocrinology 1980;106:306 – 316.
164 Döhler KD, Wuttke W: Changes with age in levels of serum gonadotrophins, prolactin and gonadal steroids in prepubertal male and female rats. Endocrinology 1975;97:898 – 907.
165 Corbier P, Picon R, Roffi J: Elévation de la testostérone chez le rat nouveau-né. C R Acad Sci D 1977;285:1247 – 1249.
166 Pang SF, Caggiula AR, Gay VL: Goodman RL, Pang CSF: Serum concentrations of testosterone, oestrogens, luteinizing hormone and follicle-stimulating hormone in male and female rats during the critical period of neural sexual differentiation. J Endocrinol 1979;80:103 – 110.
167 Butte JC, Moore JA, Kakihana R: Brain and plasma levels of testosterone, dihydrotestosterone and estradiol in the one-day-old rat. Life Sci 1979;24:2343 – 2350.
168 Gogan F, Slama A, Bizzini-Koutznetzova B, Dray F, Kordon C: Importance of perinatal testosterone in sexual differentiation in the male rat. J Endocrinol 1981;91:75 – 79.
169 Reyes FI, Boroditsky RS, Winter JSD, Faiman C: Studies on human sexual development. II. Fetal and maternal serum gonadotropin and sex steroid concentrations. J Clin Endocrinol Metab 1974;38:612 – 617.
170 Dörner G, Stahl F, Rohde W, Göretzlehner G, Wittkowski R, Saffert H: Sex-specific testosterone and FSH concentrations in amniotic fluids of mid-pregnancy. Endokrinologie 1977;70:86 – 88.
171 Ward IL, Weisz J: Maternal stress alters plasma testosterone in fetal males. Science 1980;207: 328 – 329.
172 Reddy VV, Naftolin F, Ryan KJ: Conversion of androstenedione to estrogen by neural tissues from fetal and neonatal rats. Endocrinology 1974;94:117 – 121.
173 Hutchison JB, Steimer T: Androgen metabolism in the brain: Behavioral correlates; in De Vries GJ, De Bruin JPC, Uylings HBM, Corner MA (eds): Prog Brain Res. Amsterdam, Elsevier, 1984, vol 61, pp 23 – 51.
174 Michael RP, Bonsall RW, Rees HD: The uptake of [^{3}H]testosterone and its metabolites by the brain and pituitary gland of the fetal macaque. Endocrinology 1989;124:1319 – 1326.
175 George FW, Ojeda SR: Changes in aromatase activity in the rat brain during embryonic, neonatal, and infantile development. Endocrinology 1982; 111:522 – 529.
176 Weisz J, Brown BL, Ward IL: Maternal stress decreases steroid aromatase activity in brains of male and female rat fetuses. Neuroendocrinology 1982;35:374 – 379.
177 Von Ziegler NI, Lichtensteiger W: Asymmetry of brain aromatase activity: Region and sex-specific developmental patterns. Neuroendocrinology, 1992;55:512 – 518.
178 Bakan P: Handedness and maternal smoking during pregnancy. Int J Neurosci 1991;56:161 – 168.
179 Roselli CE, Resko JA: Androgens regulate brain aromatase activity in adult male rats through a receptor mechanism. Endocrinology 1984;114: 2183 – 2189.
180 Steimer T, Hutchison JB: Is the androgen-dependent increase in preoptic estradiol-17β formation due to aromatase induction? Brain Res 1989;480:335 – 339.
181 Weaver CE, Baum MJ: Differential regulation of brain aromatase by androgen in adult and fetal ferrets. Endocrinology 1991;128:1247 – 1254.
182 King JA, Strand FL: Increased ACTH plasma levels with prenatal and postnatal nicotine administration in rats. Ann N Y Acad Sci 1988; 529;301 – 303.

Prof. W. Lichtensteiger
Institute of Pharmacology
University of Zürich
Gloriastrasse 32
CH – 8006 Zürich (Switzerland)

Dev Brain Dysfunct 1993;6:305 – 316

1019 – 5815/93/0065 – 0305$2.75/0

Antenatal Visualization of Malformations Associated with Drugs and Chemicals

Gideon Koren, Irena Nulman

The Motherisk Program, The Hospital for Sick Children and The University of Toronto, Ontario, Canada

Key Words. Malformation · Teratogens · Early diagnosis · Ultrasonography

Abstract. Some drug-induced congenital malformations can be visualized by ultrasound during pregnancy. This can help the family decide about the continuation of pregnancy and the clinician in following up the pregnancy. In this report, we summarize published data on fetal ultrasound in pregnancies exposed to drugs and chemicals.

Introduction

The ability to detect fetal malformation antenatally is important both in order to allow families to terminate such pregnancies if they so wish, and to plan for optimal fetal and/or neonatal management if pregnancy continues.

Since the thalidomide disaster in the 1950s, an increasing number of drugs and chemicals have been incriminated as causing teratogenicity or fetal toxity. As the majority of pregnant women are exposed to at least one medication during pregnancy, either before or after realizing that they are pregnant [1], the need to determine the relative risk that a certain agent will cause malformations is of utmost importance.

Data on chemically induced teratogenic risk are derived from animal studies, human case reports, or epidemiological studies. While such information is essential for assigning a relative risk to a potential teratogen, it may be of little help for medication in a specific case. Sonography has emerged as a powerful tool for antenatal detection of fetal anomalies. It is conceivable therefore that more and more pregnant women exposed to drugs and chemicals will be referred for diagnosis of or to rule out malformations associated with these agents. Currently, pregnant women who attend our Motherisk Clinic for antenatal

Table 1. Common drugs

Drug	Central nervous system	Cardiovascular	Skeleton
Acetaminophen (overdose)			clubfoot
Acetazolamide			sacrococcygeal teratoma
Acetylsalicylic acid	intracranial hemorrhage		
Albuteral		fetal tachycardia	
Alcohol	microcephaly	heart malformations	short nose, hypoplastic maxilla, small mandible, poorly formed orbites, incomplete skull ossification
Amantadine		single ventricle with pulmonary atresia	
Aminopterin[1]	meningoencephalocele, incomplete skull ossification, brachycephaly, anencephaly		hypoplasia of thumb and fibula, clubfoot, syndactyly, cranium abnormal, small mandible
Amitriptyline	hydrocephalus		small mandible
Amobarbital	Anencephaly	heart malformations	
Antithyroid drugs			scalp and finger-toe abnormalities
Azathioprine[1]	cerebral hemorrhage, plagiocephaly	atrial septal defects, pulmonary valvular stenosis	
Betamethasone	reduced head circumference		
Bromides	microcephaly	heart malformations	
Busulfan			
Caffeine			musculoskeletal defects
Captopril			
Carbon monoxide[1]	cerebral atrophy, hydrocephalus, microcephaly	fetal bradycardia	

Table 1. (Continued)

Extremities	Gastrointestinal	Genitourinary	Miscellaneous	Source
dislocation of the hip			polyhydramnios	CR
				CR
oral cleft			growth retardation	PS
				CR
				PS
	cleft lip/palate, diaphragmatic hernia	renal defects, hypospadias, labial hypoplasia	growth retardation, microphthalmia	CR
				PS
				CR
abnormal position of extremities, short forearms, talipes, clubfoot		cleft lip/palate	low-set ears	CR
limb reduction, swelling of hands and feet		urinary retention, hypospadias		CR
severe limb deformities, hip dislocation, polydactyly, clubfoot	oral cleft	intersex, hypospadias, hydrocele	soft tissue deformity of neck, accessory auricle, inguinal hernia	PS
				CR
			goiter, aplasia cutis	CR
limb reduction, preaxial polydactyly		hypospadias	growth retardation	RS
				CR
			premature babies	PS
polydactyly, clubfoot, dislocation of hip	gastrointestinal anomalies		growth retardation	CR
	pyloric stenosis, cleft palate, bipolar spleen, hepatic subcapsular calcification	hydronephrosis, kidney/ureter anomalies	microphthalmia, growth retardation	CR
leg reduction		hydronephrosis		PS
				CR
	renal defects, renal insufficiency		stillbirth	CR
			stillbirth	CR
				PS

Table 1. (Continued)

Drug	Central nervous sistem	Cardiovascular	Skeleton
Carbamazepine	meningomyelocele, spina bifida, decreased head circumference	atrial septal defect, patent ductus arteriosus	nose hypoplasia, hypertelorism
Chlordiazepoxide	microcephaly	heart malformations	
Chloroquine	tetralogy of Fallot		
Chlorpheniramine	hydrocephalus		
Chlorpropamide	microcephaly, anencephaly	atrial septal defect	vertebral anomalies
Clomiphene	meningomyelocele, hydrocephalus, microcephaly, anencephaly, neural tube defect		
Codeine	hydrocephalus	heart malformations	musculoskeletal malformations
Cortisone	hydrocephalus, cyclopia	ventricular septal defect, coarctation of aorta	
Coumadin[1]	encephalocele, anencephaly, spina bifida, agenesis of corpus callosum, Dandy-Walker malformation	heart malformations	nasal hypoplasia, scoliosis, skeletal deformities, absence of clavicles
Cyclophosphamide[1]	microcephaly	tetralogy of Fallot	dysmorphic facies, flattened nasal bridge
Cytarabine	anencephaly	tetralogy of Fallot	
Daunorubicin[1]	anencephaly	tetralogy of Fallot	
Dextroamphetamine	exencephaly, hydrocephalus, microcephaly	heart malformations, atrial septal defect	
Diazepam	spina bifida	heart malformations	hypertelorism
Diphenhydramine		ventricular septal defects	
Disulfiram			vertebral fusion

Table 1. (Continued)

Extremities	Gastrointestinal	Genitourinary	Miscellaneous	Source
polydactylia, talipes, hip dislocation	anal atresia, cleft lip	ambiguous genitalia	inguinal hernia	PS CR
	duodenal atresia, Meckel's diverticulum			RS
			Wilms' tumor, hemyhypertrophy	CR
polydactyly, dislocation of hip	gastrointestinal defects		eye and ear defects, inguinal hernia	PS
dysmorphic hand and fingers	stricture of lower ileum, cleft palate		preauricular sinus, ear tags, perinatal death	CR
syndactyly, clubfoot, polydactyly	esophageal atresia, cleft lip/palate	hypospadias, ovarian dysplasia	hemangiomas	CR RS
dislocated hip	pyloric stenosis, oral cleft, umbilical and inguinal hernia	genitourinary abnormality	respiratory pathways malformations	PS RS
clubfoot	cleft lip, gastroschisis			CR
stippled epiphyses, chondroplasia punctata, short phalanges, toe defects	incomplete rotation of gut, asplenia, cleft palate	single kidney	growth retardation, bleeding, microphthalmia	CR RS
four toes on each foot, hypoplastic midphalanx, syndactyly, absence nails/thumbs	inguinal and/or umbilical hernia, imperforate anus, rectovaginal fistula		hemangiomas, growth retardation, microphthalmia	CR
lobster claw malformations, missing toes, syndactyly			growth retardation, atresia of external auditory canal	CR
syndactyly			growth retardation	CR
dislocation of hip, absence of arm, syndactyly, absence of thumbs	biliary atresia, cleft lip/palate	urogenital defects	growth retardation	CR RS
clubfoot	cleft palate/lip, inguinal hernia	renal defects	hemangiomas, growth retardation	PS CR
	cleft palate, inguinal hernia	hypospadias, genitourinary malformations other than hypospadias		PS CR
clubfoot, radial aplasia, phocomelia	tracheoesophageal fistula			CR PS

Table 1. (Continued)

Drug	Central nervous sistem	Cardiovascular	Skeleton
Diuretics			
Estrogens		heart malformations	
Ethanol[1]	microcephaly	ventricular septal defect, atrial septal defect, double outlet of right ventricle, pulmonary atresia, dextrocardia, patent ductus arteriosus, tetralogy of Fallot	short nose, hypoplastic philtrum, micrognathia, pectus excavatum, radioulnar synostosis, bifid xyphoid, scoliosis
Ethosuximide	hydrocephalus, microcephaly		short neck
Fluorouracil	hydrocephalus, anencephaly	hypoplasia of aorta, lung	
Folic acid (absence)	neural tube defect		
Fluphenazine			poor ossification of frontal bone, ocular hypertelorism
Haloperidol		aortic valve defect	
Heparin[1]			
Hormones, progestogenic	anencephaly, hydrocephalus	tetralogy of Fallot, truncus arteriosus, ventricular septal defect	spina bifida
Imipramine	exencephaly		
Indomethacin		premature closure of ductus arteriosus, tricuspid regurgitation	
Isoniazid	meningomyelocele		spina bifida
Lithium	hydrocephalus, meningomyelocele	ventricular septal defect, Ebstein's anomaly, mitral atresia, patent ductus arteriosus, dextrocardia	spina bifida

Table 1. (Continued)

Extremities	Gastrointestinal	Genitourinary	Miscellaneous	Source
limb reduction				CR, PS
wormian bones, dislocated hips, absent tibia, polydactyly	cleft palate	V-Vertebral, A-Anal, C-Cardiac, T-Tracheal, E-Esophageal, R-Renal or Radial, L-Limb	eye and ear anomalies	PS CR
	oral cleft, diaphragmatic hernia	renal defects, hypospadias, labial hypoplasia	growth retardation	CR RS PS
	oral cleft			CR
radial aplasia, absent thumbs and fingers	aplasia of esophagus, duodenum, absent appendix, imperforate anus/cloaca, hypoplasia of duodenum, bile duct	hypoplasia of uterus	hypoplasia of thymus	CR
				CR PS RS
	oral cleft, imperforate anus	rectouretral fistula, hypospadias		PS CR
limb deformities				RS
			bleeding	RS
absence of thumbs	inguinal hernia	hypospadias, ambiguous genitalia		RS CR
limb reduction	cleft palate, diaphragmatic hernia	renal cystic dysplasia	adrenal hypoplasia, defective abdominal muscles	CR
phocomelia	intestinal perforation and bleeding	reduced fetal urine output, oliguria	stillbirth, hemorrhage, oligohydramnios	CR
talipes				PS
clubfoot, dislocated hip			stillbirth	CR RS PS

Table 1. (Continued)

Drug	Central nervous sistem	Cardiovascular	Skeleton
Lysergic acid diethylamide	hydrocephalus, encephalocele, meningomyelocele	tetralogy of Fallot	spina bifida occulta
Meclizine	meningocele, hydrocephalus, spina bifida	hypoplasia cardis, hypoplastic left heart	
Meprobamate		heart malformations	
Methotrexate[1]	anencephaly, oxycephaly, absence of frontal bone, large fontanelles	dextrocardia	hypoplastic mandible, hypertelorism
Methyl mercury[1]	microcephaly, asymmetric head		
Metronidazole[1]	brain defects, holotelencephaly		midline facial defects
Nortriptyline			
Oral contraceptives	meningomyelocele, hydrocephalus, anencephaly	heart malformations	vertebral malformations
Paramethadione	tetralogy of Fallot		
Penicillamine	hydrocephalus, intraventricular hemorrhage	ventricular septal defect	small mandible
Phenobarbital	hydrocephalus, meningomyelocele		
Phenothiazine	microcephaly		
Phenylephrine			
Phenylpropanolamine			pectus excavatum
Phenytoin[1]	microcephaly	heart malformations	rib-sternal abnormalities, wide fontanelle, broad alveolar ridge, short neck, hypertelorism, spotted calcification in skull, fontanelle and sagittal suture, webbed neck, small mandible, short nose, broad nasal bridge
Polychlorinated biphenyl[1]	smaller head sizes		

Table 1. (Continued)

Extremities	Gastrointestinal	Genitourinary	Miscellaneous	Source
limb deficiencies, bilateral defects of limbs			neuroblastoma	PS CR
	imperforate anus pyloric stenosis	renal hypoplasia	respiratory pathway defects, eye and ear defects, inguinal hernia	PS CR
dysplastic hips			abdominal wall defect	CR PS
long webbed fingers, absence of digits, abnormal ribs			growth retardation, low-set ears	CR
				CR
dislocated hip, limb abnormalities	oral cleft	genital defects, hydrocele		CR PS
limb reduction				CR
limb reduction	tracheoesophageal + anal malformations	renal malformations	growth retardation	RS CR
			growth retardation	PS
dislocated hip, bilateral clubfoot, limb deformations	pyloric stenosis, perforated bowel		growth retardation, stillbirth, inguinal hernia, low-set ears	CR
digital anomalies	cleft palate, ileal atresia		growth retardation, pulmonary hypoplasia	CR
syndactyly, clubfoot	omphalocele, abdominal distension			CR PS
syndactyly, clubfoot, dislocation of hip	umbilical hernia	eye and ear abnormalities		PS
polydactyly, dislocation of hip		hypospadias		PS
hypoplastic distal phalanges and nails, digitalized thumb, dislocated hip	cleft palate/lip, diaphragmatic hernia		growth retardation, neurotumors, low-set ears	CR PS RS
			stillbirth, growth retardation	PS

Table 1. (Continued)

Drug	Central nervous sistem	Cardiovascular	Skeleton
Procarbazine[1]	cerebral hemorrhage	ventricular septal defect	oligodactyly and other finger and limb abnormalities
Quinine	hydrocephalus	heart malformations	facial defects, vertebral anomalies
Retinoic acid[1]	hydrocephalus, microcephaly	heart malformations	malformations of cranium, ear, face, ribs, micrognatia
Spermicides			
Sulfonamide			
Tetracycline			clubfoot
Thalidomide[1]		heart malformations	spine malformation
Thioguanine		tetralogy of Fallot	
Tobacco			
Tolbutamide		heart malformations	
Trifluoperazine		transposition of great arteries	
Trimethadione[1]	microcephaly	atrial septal defect, ventricular septal defect	low-set ears, broad nasal bridge
Valproic acid[1]	lumbosacral meningomyelocele, microcephaly, wide fontanelle	tetralogy of Fallot, ventricular septal defect, valvular aortic stenosis	depressed nasal bridge, hypoplastic nose, low-set ears, small mandibles

Since only malformations than can be visualized by current ultrasonographic techniques are listed, the guide cannot be used as a complete list of drug-induced teratogenicity. CR = Case reports; RS = retrospective studies; PS = prospective studies; AS = animal studies.

Table 1. (Continued)

Extremities	Gastrointestinal	Genitourinary	Miscellaneous	Source
		malformed kidneys	growth retardation, multiple hemangiomas	CR
dysmelias, limb deformities	gastrointestinal abnormalities	urogenital abnormalities	hernias	CR
			stillbirth, thymic defects, microphthalmia	RS PS
limb reduction, hypoplasia of limb or part of it, foot defects		hypospadias		PS CR RS
hypoplasia of limb or part of it, clubfoot		urethral obstructions	adrenal atrophy, benign tumors	PS CR
limb reduction (amelia, phocomelia), hypoplasia	duodenal stenosis or atresia, pyloric stenosis	hypospadias	inguinal hernia	PS CR
missing digits			microtia	CR
limb and digit abnormalities			fetal death, growth retardation	CR
			growth retardation	PS
finger-toe syndactyly, absent toes, accessory thumb	cleft palate, tracheo-oesophageal fistula	renal anomalies	stillbirth	RS
phocomelia				CR
malformed hands, clubfoot	esophageal atresia, imperforate anus, oral cleft	hypospadias, kidney and ureter abnormalities, ambiguous genitalia	growth retardation, inguinal hernia	CR PS
limb, finger, toe, nail abnormalities	oral cleft, duodenal atresia, inguinal hernia		growth retardation, umbilical hernia	CR

[1] Proved to be teratogenic.

Reproduced from Koren et al. (Amer J Obstet Gynecol 1987;156:79 – 85), with permission of CV Mosby Company.

counseling of drug-chemical exposure are scheduled for a level 2 sonographic evaluation in 17 – 18 weeks of gestation if there is an increased risk for malformations or when gestational age is not known.

This guide aims at providing the sonographer with a practical list of malformations that have been described in association with specific drugs or chemicals. It is an updated version of our original publication several years ago [1].

Methodological Considerations

Two groups of agents are included [1]. Common drugs and chemicals that have been associated with the malformations are listed. In many cases the incriminating data are controversial; hence the inclusion of a certain malformation in this guide by no means suggests that we are convinced that the agent is a teratogen. Because of the heterogeneity of the data, the source of information is mentioned (for instance, case reports, retrospective or prospective studies) [2]. Drugs and chemicals that have been proved beyond doubt as teratogens are maked (see table 1).

Table 1 includes only malformations that can be visualized by current ultrasonographic techniques and cannot be used as a complete list of drug-induced teratogenicity. This data in this guide have been extracted from currently available literature [2 – 9].

Certain points with respect to the ultrasound examination itself should be stressed. It is probably best carried out by a physician ultrasonographer who has had significant experience in looking at fetuses. A very meticulous technique and high-resolution real-time equipment should be used. The examination is best recorded on videotape so that it can be reviewed as needed. A great deal of patience is required in this type of study, especially when one is examining the face, digits, and heart. At the outset of the examination it should be explained to the patient that the examination may take some time to complete and that more than one sitting may be required.

References

1 Koren G, Brill Edwards M, Miskin M: Fetal malformations associated with drugs and chemicals: Visualization by sonography; in Koren G (ed): Maternal-Fetal Toxicology. New York, Marcel Dekker, 1990, pp 297 – 307.
2 Schardein J: Chemically Induced Birth Defects. New York, Marcel Dekker, 1985.
3 Fabro S: Reproductive Toxicology. A Medical Letter. Washington, Reproductive Toxicology Center, 1984.
4 Mattison DR: Reproductive Toxicology. New York, Liss, 1983.
5 Briggs GG, Bodendorfer TW, Freeman RK, Yaffe SJ: Drugs in Pregnancy and Lactation, ed 3. Baltimore, Williams & Wilkins, 1990.
6 Heinonen OP, Slone D, Shapiro S: Birth Defects and Drugs in Pregnancy. Littleton, PSG Publishing, 1977.
7 Shepard TH: Catalog of Teratogenic Agents, ed 6. Baltimore, John Hopkins University Press, 1989.
8 Onnis A, Grella P: The Biochemical Effects of Drugs in Pregnancy. Chichester, Ellis Horwood Ltd, 1984.
9 Berglund F, et al: Drug use during pregnancy and breast-feeding. A classification system for drug information. Acta Obstet Gynecol Scand Suppl 1984;126:1 – 55.

Dr. Gideon Koren
The Hospital for Sick Children
Department of Paediatrics
555 University Avenue
Toronto, Ontario M5G 1X8 (Canada)

Dev Brain Dysfunct
ISSN 1019–5815
DBDYEV
6(4–5) 193–316 (1993)

Developmental Brain Dysfunction

Impact of Prenatal Teratogenic Exposure on Phenotype and Brain Function

The updated reviews featured in this publication provide readers with helpful information on the impact of diverse teratogens on fetal development. Clinical in focus, the reviews aim to help clinicians deal with problems during pregnancy and after birth which arise because of teratogens. Specific attention is paid to potential brain damage caused by hyperthermia, maternal diabetes, exposure to oral anticoagulants (Coumarin derivatives), exposure to alcohol, diphenylhydantoin, and cigarette smoking. The final paper provides practical advice regarding the ultrasonic diagnosis of fetal teratogenic damage. Clinical geneticists, medical embryologists, paediatricians and obstetricians will find these reviews helpful for the genetic counselling of patients at risk for fetal damage through teratogens.

Cover illustration

Proposed biochemical mechanism giving rise to the combination of features present in children with the so-called pseudowarfarin embryopathy secondary to vitamin K epoxide reductase deficiency. See paper by Pauli et al., p. 229.

KARGER